Chemistry
12901

Laboratory Manual

Department of Chemistry

2018

PURDUE
UNIVERSITY

 macmillan learning
curriculum solutions

Printed in the United States of America

10 9 8 7 6 5 4 3 2 1

ISBN 978-1-5339-0467-6

Macmillan Learning Curriculum Solutions
14903 Pilot Drive
Plymouth, MI 48170
www.macmillanlearning.com

MeyerJ 0467-6 F18-S

Sustainability
Hayden-McNeil's standard paper stock uses a minimum of 30% post-consumer waste. We offer higher % options by request, including a 100% recycled stock. Additionally, Hayden-McNeil Custom Digital provides authors with the opportunity to convert print products to a digital format. Hayden-McNeil is part of a larger sustainability initiative through Macmillan Learning. Visit http://sustainability.macmillan.com to learn more.

bedford/st. martin's • hayden-mcneil
w.h. freeman • worth publishers

Chemistry 12901
Table of Contents

How to Be Successful in CHM 12901: A Guide to Using Laboratory Equipment and Instrumentation

Chapters

NOTES

Working in a Group

By Dave Eichinger

Why Work in a Group?

Throughout the semester your lab work will be completed in a group. Why do we put so much emphasis on group work?

Our reasons are really twofold. First, both you and the other members of your lab group will understand the labs better. Educational research has shown that cooperative group work is an effective means for teaching/learning science (and almost any other subject) and can help increase your understanding of the material. *Every time you have to explain something to a group mate, the better you will understand the concept.* And, for those times when you find yourself clueless (it happens to all of us from time to time), group work gives you the opportunity to have someone besides your graduate instructor or professor explain the concept to you. Sometimes your group mates will have a common experience that will make a great memory association or analogy for you that is unknown to the staff. This means there are benefits for all group members *if the group is functioning properly.*

Building a Working Group

Although most humans are by nature social creatures, cooperative group work is not something that comes without effort. Such group activities require that a sense of trust be built between members, as well as a feeling of **shared responsibility**. This means *a responsibility to carry your own weight in the group, as well as a responsibility to all of the other members of the group.* In such a case, no one group member gets frustrated and rushes on ahead of the group, and the group NEVER leaves any of its members behind. This may not always be easy. What do you do when you have someone in your group that you don't like? Or who doesn't like you? How do you deal with group members who refuse to help you out when you are confused?

Some words of advice: slow down and remember that your group members are just as new at this as you are. Learning to be a member of the group, rather than a competing individual in the learning process, is a new experience for nearly everyone in this class. This should be seen as a professional experience, not a time for making social contacts. It does not matter whether or not your group mates are the kind of people you would most likely choose to socialize with on Friday night. You will find that you can still work with these individuals.

Finally, remember that in group work we expect *all group members to take responsibility for keeping all of their group mates up to speed* and to take personal responsibility for contributing their maximum effort. "The whole is greater than the sum of its parts" is especially true when working in groups.

My Group Can't Get Along

Very rarely do we find a group that actually cannot work. What we do find are groups with members who are not communicating effectively. If you think your group is having problems, sit down and talk things over as a group. Agree on some basic rules of conduct and responsibility within your group, and make a commitment to each other. Then try again. If you find you are still having problems, you may need help from someone with an "outside" perspective. Make an appointment when your entire group can meet with your graduate instructor, course supervisor, or professor to talk things over. Don't let problems linger or fester, but do try to work things out among yourselves first.

Most of all, relax and enjoy interacting with new people. Think of this as preparation for the "real" world where you will be required to work closely with people in many different settings. You will not always like all of those people, but you may find that you enjoy interacting with people who are very different from yourself. Relax, enjoy yourself, and have fun exploring the world around you.

Working as a Team

Working as a team requires that different members assume different responsibilities. There are many ways to divide responsibility of work in a project, and one suggested way is to assign roles which rotate among group members from week to week. For example, with a four-person group you might want to assign the roles of:

- Manager

- Technician

- Quality Control Officer

- Safety Officer

While each member of the group helps with the lab work, each individual accepts the major responsibility for ensuring that a portion of the project is done properly.

Group Lab Reports

You will be required to turn in group lab reports. It is your responsibility as a group to ensure that everyone whose name is on the report participated as fully as possible in the project.

There are several different ways a group lab report can be generated:

- Everyone in the group can gather together and work on the entire report at the same time.

- Individuals can take responsibility for different portions of the lab report. Remember that the entire report must be coherent, however.

- The group can assign one individual to do the report. This responsibility must be rotated within the group from week to week.

- Each member of the group can write his/her own report and then the group can compare the reports and decide which one report to submit as a group.

NOTES

NOTES

Laboratory Projects

Laboratory projects consist of three components:

- Preparing before lab so that you have an idea about the goals, procedures, and computations in order to carry out the lab work correctly and efficiently.

- Making and keeping organized, legible records of the systematic observations and measurements of the physical and chemical properties of substances using standard laboratory analysis techniques in a safe manner.

- Preparing a report that involves analysis of your observations and measurements and that also reflects an understanding of the procedures, techniques, and chemical systems in relationship to the chemical concepts and principles covered in lecture and the textbook.

Laboratory Records: The Lab Notebook

You will be expected to maintain a complete lab notebook for the laboratory work that you do in CHM 12901. A laboratory notebook is where you keep an official record of everything you do, observe, measure, etc., while in lab. These records are *notes*, not a full report, although they must be legible and well organized.

Laboratory notes and records are traditionally kept in duplicate and one copy kept in a different place than the original should the original be lost.

Before Lab. Prelab exercises are to be done before going to lab! The purpose of prelab exercises is to help you be prepared and understand the goals of each project before you begin work in the laboratory. Each student is individually responsible for answering the prelab exercises in his/her laboratory notebook and submitting the perforated pages from his/her lab notebook where the answers are written to his/her graduate instructor at the beginning of the laboratory period for which the experiment is scheduled. Late answers to prelab questions will not be accepted.

During Lab. You are to record observations, measurements, calculations, etc., completed during the laboratory period. This must be done in an organized and legible manner. Organize information into tables whenever possible.

At the End of Each Laboratory Period. You are to give your graduate instructor the duplicate copy of all pages from your laboratory notebook on which you recorded observations, measurements, calculations, etc., during that laboratory period.

Changing any observations or measurements after you leave the laboratory is considered to be cheating and will be dealt with accordingly.

Guidelines for the Laboratory Notebook

- The required lab notebook for Chemistry 12901 is a carbonless copy notebook.

- Record the title of the project, the date on which it was done, the observations and measurements made while doing the experiment in the notebook.

- All entries are to be written in pen.

- All entries in the laboratory notebook must be legible.

- When you make a mistake while entering observations or measurements into the laboratory notebook, cross out the mistake with a single line so that the erroneous entry remains legible.

- Date and sign each page of the laboratory notebook upon completing the work.

Laboratory Reports

Lab reports depend heavily on the information in your lab notes, but additional information from other sources may be necessary to prepare a complete report. In a lab report, you take the notes and organize them into a presentable and readable summary of the work that you completed.

Laboratory reports allow you to illustrate and demonstrate your knowledge of chemistry in a different way than do multiple choice exams or quizzes. Unlike hourly exams, however, laboratory reports focus on a specific or narrow topic and you can discuss the topics with others as you prepare the report. In a lab report, you are expected to link ideas, procedures, and analyses to the theory and problem-solving strategies you study in lectures and read in the textbook. It may be necessary to use and apply information from more than one chapter in your textbook to complete a lab project.

 Each team will turn in a single lab report for the team projects (unless otherwise stated). While you are encouraged to discuss concepts with other members of your class, each written report is to be a unique effort by your team. All members of your team share the responsibility for writing lab reports that honestly reflect your work. It is also your responsibility as a team to ensure that everyone whose name is on the report participated in preparing it.

Guidelines

General Information

a. Lab report is due in lab one week after experiment is completed.

b. Submit one lab report per group.

c. All group members need to meet outside of lab as a group.

d. Type report in Times New Roman font size 12.

e. Each section of the lab report should be clearly labeled.

f. Write in the third person, past tense.

Title Page

a. Experiment title (not just chapter number).

b. Date report is turned in.

c. Lab group member names (who were present for the lab experiment).

d. Section number.

Purpose

a. Describe purpose of the experiment in your own words (1–2 sentences).

b. Do NOT copy the purpose from the lab manual word for word (plagiarism is not tolerated!).

Procedure

a. Do NOT rewrite the procedure of the experiment, but reference your lab manual as shown below:

    Title, Name of Book, Department, copyright date, page #

b. Each prelab will contain a full handwritten procedure.

Results

Raw Data

a. Summarize all data collected in organized tables and/or graphs.

b. All tables and graphs need to have descriptive titles.

c. All table headings and graph axes should be *labeled appropriately with units*.

d. Display the equation and R^2 value for all trendlines on graphs.

e. Data should be organized in the same order you collected it in.

f. If you are unsure of which data to include, check your lab manual first.

Analysis

a. The procedure gives you instructions on how to analyze the data collected.

b. Show all steps for each calculation (if a calculation is repeated several times only show one example, then present the results of the calculations in an organized table).

c. Please note: not all labs will require calculations but will ALWAYS require some type of analysis.

d. Determine the standard deviation in graphs when appropriate.

Postlab (Discussion Questions)

a. Answer ALL discussion questions in the lab manual in complete sentences.

b. Discussion questions can have several parts; make sure you answer all of them thoroughly.

c. Number all discussion questions as they are numbered in your lab manual (you do not need to copy the question).

d. If you made a mistake in your procedure, you MUST discuss the source of your error at the end of this section in a paragraph titled "Error Analysis."

Other Important Reminders

a. Proofread your labs!

b. Write in complete sentences and paragraphs.

c. Be concise—avoid extra adjectives and descriptions if they are not needed.

Safety Policies in Chemistry Labs at Purdue

©Hayden-McNeil, LLC

Concerns

The safety of everyone in the active learning environment is taken seriously, and your failure to comply with the safety regulations will affect your course grade.

Safety policies MUST be followed in the laboratories by everyone in a laboratory. Everyone's safety is a primary concern in laboratory instructional situations and must be taken very seriously by everyone in a lab. We don't establish and enforce rules to harass students, graduate instructors, or staff, but we must comply with EPA regulations to create a safe working environment for everyone. Ultimately it is everyone's responsibility to watch out for everyone's safety in a laboratory setting. The rules we follow are based on many years of teaching experience in general chemistry labs.

If you are dismissed from lab for violation of safety regulations, not wearing splash goggles for the entire time you are in lab, or for not being dressed properly for lab work, you will:

- be dismissed from lab for the day.
- get a grade of zero for that lab.
- have that lab counted as a missed lab.

Safety and Dress Regulations

Chemical Splash Goggles

Each student must own and wear approved chemical splash goggles (not safety glasses) *in the laboratory at all times*, including the day of checkout.

Splash goggles can be purchased at the local bookstores, the chemistry storeroom, or outside of WTHR 200 during the first week of the semester.

©Hayden-McNeil, LLC

Appropriate Clothing

Chemistry department regulations require you to wear clothing that protects your skin and eyes from harm as a result of an accident in the laboratory. Proper clothing for laboratory work protects your skin from neck to your ankles, feet, and toes when you are sitting, standing, or reaching. You are expected to arrive at lab properly dressed for lab work. You will not be given time to go away, change clothes, and return to lab.

©Hayden-McNeil, LLC

Acceptable footwear (with socks).

Unacceptable clothing for lab work includes, but is not limited to:

- sleeveless or bare midriff tops
- clothes that are ripped or have holes in the fabric that expose your skin
- shorts, short skirts
- open-toed and/or open-heeled shoes and sandals (with or without socks)
- ballet-type or house slippers
- flip-flops

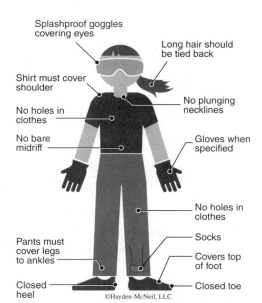

Splashproof goggles covering eyes

Long hair should be tied back

Shirt must cover shoulder

No plunging necklines

No holes in clothes

No bare midriff

Gloves when specified

No holes in clothes

Pants must cover legs to ankles

Socks

Covers top of foot

Closed heel

Closed toe

©Hayden-McNeil, LLC

Proper attire for lab.

Gloves

Gloves serve two purposes: not only do they protect your skin from potential hazardous materials, they can prevent transfer of potentially hazardous materials to locations outside the lab. You will be required to wear protective gloves for many lab activities. When you leave lab, take the gloves off and recycle them.

Get new gloves when you return to lab.

Contact Lenses

Wearing contact lenses in the laboratory is not a wise idea; you are encouraged to wear glasses instead. If you wear contact lenses in the laboratory, you need to inform your teaching assistant of this at the beginning of the semester.

Hair

If your hair is longer than shoulder length you must tie it behind your head in order to avoid accidental contact with open flames or chemicals that might be on the lab bench. Rubber bands are available in the laboratory.

Food and Beverages (not allowed)

You may not eat, drink, or bring food into the laboratory. This includes water bottles. Water faucets are in the halls. If you have a medical condition where you must eat during a lab time you will need to have that documented at the Adaptive Services Office in Young Hall and discuss any arrangements to be made with the course coordinator in BRWN 1144.

Electronics

The only electronic equipment allowed in the lab will be calculators and any equipment being used for instruction and learning. Cell phones, iPods, etc., are distractions for everyone and are simply inappropriate for group learning situations.

Main Fume Hoods

The main fume hoods are located along one side of the lab. The fume hood consists of an enclosure and an exhaust fan that helps remove chemical fumes, vapors, gasses, and dust to protect against exposure to hazardous materials.

Some of the reagents used in an experiment may be corrosive, toxic, or have strong odors and will usually be placed in one of the main fume hoods. Transferring these reagents while in a fume hood reduces the risk of exposure to hazardous materials.

- To use the fume hood, raise the door (called a sash) no higher than the height indicated on the yellow tag located to the left of the door.

- Do not lean into the hood with your head inside the fume hood.

- Materials should be at least 6" inside the fume hood.

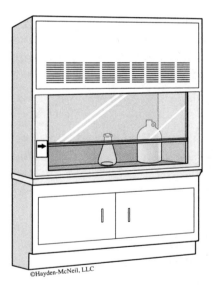

©Hayden-McNeil, LLC

Student Bench Hoods

- The student bench hood provides some protection against exposure to hazardous vapors while at the student bench.

- Student bench hoods are stored in the cabinets under the main hoods.

- Place the student bench hood against a bench exhaust vent found on the student bench.

- Keep chemicals and apparatus inside the student bench hood.

Disposal of Hazardous Materials

You will be required to follow the instructions printed in your lab manual or given to you by your teaching assistant and other staff members for appropriate disposal of any hazardous materials.

There are standard waste containers in the lab as well as special ones for waste generated by the specific experiment.

There are waste baskets in the front and rear of the lab for the disposal of items like paper towels. **NO CHEMICALS OR GLASS ARE TO BE PUT IN THESE WASTE BASKETS.**

Broken and waste glassware must be placed into the glass disposal box at the front of the lab. **NO CHEMICALS OR GLOVES ARE TO BE PUT IN GLASS DISPOSAL BOX.**

There may be waste containers provided for the collection of materials that cannot be disposed down the sink. These will normally be located in the first main hood. Chemical waste must only be disposed of in the container designated for that waste, since chemical incompatibility can result in explosion and fire. If you are not sure where to dispose of your waste, ask your TA to help you. If a waste container is full, inform your TA so he or she can request another one. Use only a few milliliters to rinse out hazardous waste from glassware into waste containers so as to not substantially increase the volume of chemical waste.

NOTES

Standard Laboratory Practices

1. Know the locations of eyewash stations, fire extinguishers, and the safety shower.

2. Check glassware. Check all glassware for chips or cracks prior to use. Replace chipped or cracked glassware immediately.

3. Read reagent bottle labels carefully. Make sure you use the correct chemical or reagent.

4. Keep caps on reagent and waste bottles at all times, except when in use.

5. Minimize waste by estimating how much reagent (solid or liquid) you need and only taking that amount or slightly more.

6. Do not pipet directly from a reagent bottle. Always use a beaker to pour out some reagent and take it back to your work area. (The exception is when a dedicated glass pipet is attached to the bottle for this purpose.)

7. You may dispense solids directly from the reagent bottle using a clean metal spatula. Place a paper weighing cup or other container on the balance and then transfer solid reagent directly from the reagent bottle into the weighing container. Do not pour out an unknown mass of solid into a weighing cup and then transfer it to a weighing container as this practice results in a lot of waste.

8. Do not pour anything back into reagent bottles. If you have unused reagent, share it with a classmate or dispose of it appropriately.

9. When disposing of a chemical in the sink, flush the drains thoroughly with lots of running water.

10. Practice good housekeeping:

    • Store all personal belongings (coats, book bags, etc.) at the coat rack at the front of the lab, or on the bench at the back of the lab (under the windows).

NOTES

- Keep benches, floors, and aisles clear of all materials not being used.
- Clean up spills promptly.
- Properly dispose of all waste according to the instructions in your lab manual or given by your instructor.
- Dispose of broken glass in the broken glass container.
- Clean shared glassware and rinse it with deionized water before returning it to the appropriate location(s).
- Return shared equipment to the appropriate location(s).
- Check and clean the balances at the end of the lab period.
- Dispose of trash or recycle unused papers.
- Wipe off benches at the end of the lab period.
- Make sure your lab drawer is locked before leaving lab.
- Wash your hands before leaving the lab.

How to Be Successful in CHM 12901: A Guide to Using Laboratory Equipment and Instrumentation

Lab Equipment

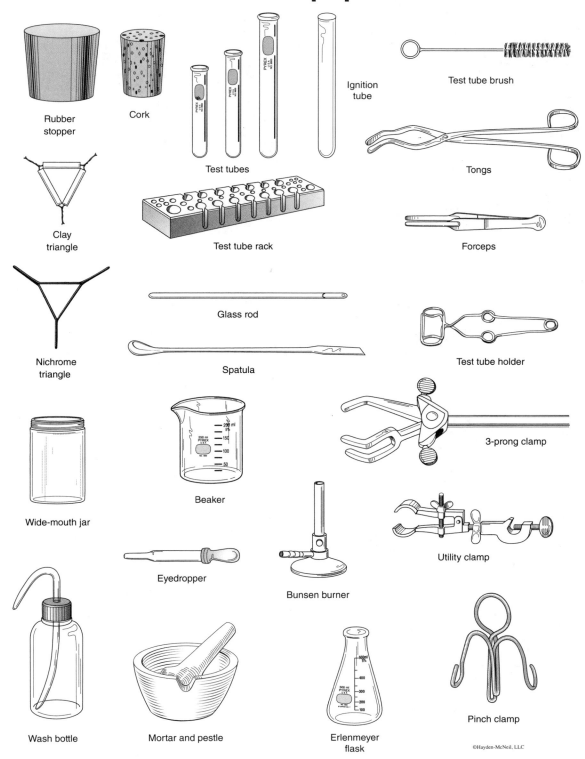

Rubber stopper

Cork

Test tubes

Ignition tube

Test tube brush

Tongs

Clay triangle

Test tube rack

Forceps

Nichrome triangle

Glass rod

Spatula

Test tube holder

Wide-mouth jar

Beaker

3-prong clamp

Eyedropper

Bunsen burner

Utility clamp

Wash bottle

Mortar and pestle

Erlenmeyer flask

Pinch clamp

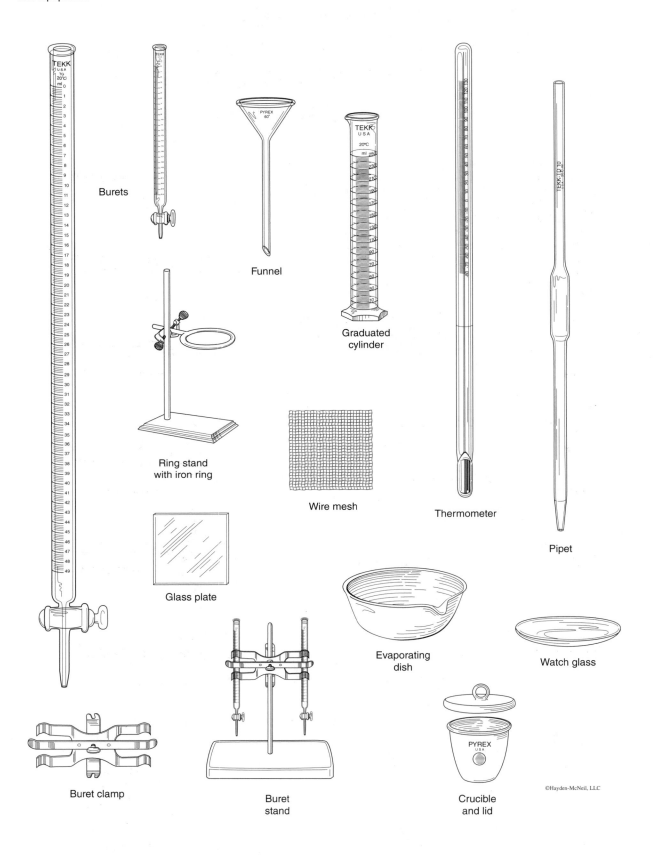

Burets

Funnel

Graduated
cylinder

Ring stand
with iron ring

Wire mesh

Thermometer

Pipet

Glass plate

Evaporating
dish

Watch glass

Buret clamp

Buret
stand

Crucible
and lid

©Hayden-McNeil, LLC

The Analytical Balance

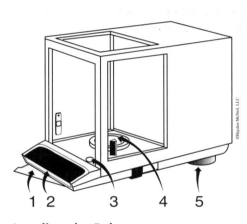

1. Brief operating instructions

2. Single control bar

3. Level indicator

4. Weighing pan/windshield ring

5. Leveling screw

1 2   3   4   5

Leveling the Balance

Check the leveling bubble on the floor of the weighing chamber. If the bubble is centered, go to the next step. Center the leveling bubble by turning the leveling screws (5) on the bottom and toward the rear of the balance.

Turning on the Balance

Close all weighing chamber doors and briefly press the control bar (2) on the front of the balance or press the "ON" button. Within a few seconds, the balance will display a set of zeros. If zeros do not appear in all the digits, press the control bar again.

Weighing a Liquid, Powder, or Granular Substance

Always weigh these substances using a weighing container provided in the lab! Place this container on the balance pan (4). Close the chamber doors. Press the control bar briefly; the display changes to zero. This is referred to as "taring" the balance. Next, add the substance up to the desired weight. Be careful not to spill chemicals on the balance. Close the chamber doors to get an accurate reading.

NOTES

Weighing a Solid Object Directly on the Balance

When it is necessary to weigh a solid object (a metal cylinder, for example) directly on the balance, tare the balance and then carefully place the object on the pan and close all the chamber doors. The display will show you the mass of the object.

Cleaning Up

Make sure that all chemicals spilled on the balance are wiped up immediately. When in doubt, check with your graduate instructor!

Turning the Balance Off (done only at the end of the day)

To turn the balance off, lift up gently on the control bar or press the off button until the display goes dark.

 If the balance does not seem to be operating properly, tell your TA, then go to the storeroom and report the problem.

Volumetric Measurement Techniques

C

Good volumetric techniques are a critical part of accurate and precise measurements in chemistry and other scientific fields.

The detailed information below is intended to help you achieve two main goals with regard to using volumetric measuring techniques:

The first goal in an analysis procedure is to *avoid doing anything to change the concentration* of the component of interest in the solution from which an aliquot is taken or in the aliquot itself.

The second goal is to *measure aliquots accurately and make dilutions carefully*.

Standard Solution

A **standard solution** is one for which the composition is known or fixed with a given level of uncertainty. Standard solutions require very careful preparation because concentration of standards is the independent variable in spectroscopy.

For example, if we were to dissolve exactly 1.3421 grams of pure sodium carbonate (Na_2CO_3, 105.99 g/mol) in pure water and then dilute the solution to exactly 100.0 mL in a 100-mL volumetric flask with pure water, then we would have a standard solution of sodium carbonate with a concentration of 0.1267 mol/L.

$$\frac{1.3421 \text{ g Na}_2\text{CO}_3 \times \dfrac{1 \text{ mol Na}_2\text{CO}_3}{105.99 \text{ g}}}{0.100 \text{ L solution}} = 0.1267 \text{ mol Na}_2\text{CO}_3/\text{L soln.}$$

$$= 0.1267 \text{ M Na}_2\text{CO}_3$$

Unknown Solution

In **quantitative** lab work, an unknown solution is one for which the composition of one or more substances is not known to the desired degree of uncertainty. For example, it is generally recognized that ordinary vinegar contains about

5% acetic acid. However, vinegar would be considered an unknown solution if we needed to know the concentration of acetic acid to three significant figures.

Stock Solution

A stock solution refers to the main volume of solution from which you will take portions needed for the measurements. To avoid contamination, never dip anything such as a pipet into the stock solution. Always pour an amount of the solution which is slightly more than the amount needed into a small, clean, dry beaker. Never pour unused solution back into the stock solution.

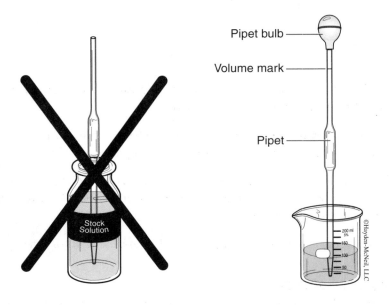

Figure C.1. Filling a pipet.

Aliquot

An **aliquot** is a measured fraction of a sample such as a standard solution, stock solution, or unknown solution. For example, if we were to measure a 25.00-mL sample from 1.0 L of a standard or unknown solution, the 25.00-mL sample would be called an aliquot of the sample. Two 25.00-mL samples would be two aliquots.

Measuring Aliquots of Solution

The two tools you will use to measure aliquots of solutions are pipets and burets.

Using a Pipet to Measure Liquid Volumes

! **WARNING!** Pipets work very much like straws. However, do not ever use your mouth to pull liquid into a pipet. This is the most common method of becoming poisoned in a chemical laboratory or becoming infected in a clinical laboratory. **Mouth pipetting is forbidden in the chemistry department.**

Cleaning and Rinsing Pipets

Pipets should first be rinsed at least once with the stock solution. The purpose of the rinse is to wet the inside walls of the pipet and remove any other solution left behind by previous use. Use a bulb (see directions below) to draw a small volume of the stock solution into the pipet and thoroughly wet the interior surface by tilting and rotating the pipet. Discard the rinse solution down the drain or into the appropriate waste container.

Filling and Delivering a Sample Using a Pipet

Collapse the bulb for aspiration by squeezing the A valve at the top of the bulb with your thumb and forefinger while squeezing the bulb into your palm with your remaining fingers. Release the valve. Holding the pipet about 2 cm from the top, gently insert the pipet into the bulb using a slight twisting motion. Do not force the pipet into the bulb; ½ cm is sufficient to make a seal between the bulb and pipet.

Place the tip of the pipet in the liquid that you wish to dispense. To pull liquid into the pipet, squeeze the S valve again until the liquid rises above the desired calibration mark. Wipe the outside of the pipet stem with a lint-free tissue.

With the calibration mark at eye level, gently squeeze the E valve on the side arm of the bulb to allow the bottom of the meniscus to line up with the desired calibration mark. Tap the tip of the pipet to the side of the vessel to remove any drops from the tip.

To dispense the liquid, squeeze the E valve on the side arm of the bulb.

If you are using a graduated pipet, allow the liquid to flow to the desired mark. If you are using a volumetric pipet, allow the liquid to flow freely until it stops. When the desired volume has been dispensed, touch the tip of the pipet to the inside of the vessel to remove any droplets that may remain. DO NOT BLOW OR FORCE ANY REMAINING LIQUID FROM THE PIPET. The volumetric pipets are calibrated "to deliver" and this takes into account the fact that a small amount of liquid remains in the tip.

Pipet safety bulb

©Hayden-McNeil, LLC

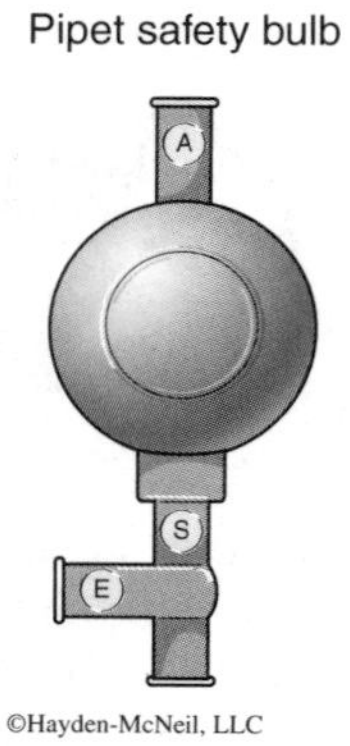

Figure C.2. 3-way safety bulb with A, S, and E labels.

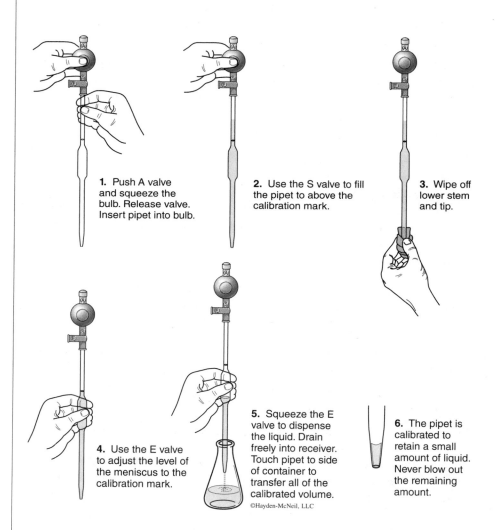

1. Push A valve and squeeze the bulb. Release valve. Insert pipet into bulb.

2. Use the S valve to fill the pipet to above the calibration mark.

3. Wipe off lower stem and tip.

4. Use the E valve to adjust the level of the meniscus to the calibration mark.

5. Squeeze the E valve to dispense the liquid. Drain freely into receiver. Touch pipet to side of container to transfer all of the calibrated volume.
©Hayden-McNeil, LLC

6. The pipet is calibrated to retain a small amount of liquid. Never blow out the remaining amount.

Figure C.3. Using a pipet.

Using a Buret to Measure Liquid Volumes

Cleaning

Assume that burets in the general chemistry lab need to be cleaned and rinsed well with deionized water before using.

The buret should be rinsed twice with a small amount of the reagent it is to hold before loading. The rinses must be disposed of in the proper manner.

Support

Special buret clamps are used to hold and support a buret to a ring stand during use. These clamps come in several shapes.

Filling a Buret

- Close the stopcock, and then tilt the buret slightly to one side and pour the liquid from a 100-mL beaker slowly down the inside wall of the buret to avoid forming air bubbles in the liquid.

- Place a small beaker under the tip of the buret and open the stopcock part way, permitting liquid to flow slowly until the buret tip is completely filled with liquid.

- If any air bubbles are present in the stopcock or buret tip, open the stopcock full in an effort to force them out. Repeat as necessary.

- Once air is removed from the stopcock and tip, fill the buret until the top of the liquid level is in the calibrated range of the buret.

- Touch the inside wall of a clean beaker to the buret tip one time. **Do not wipe the tip.**

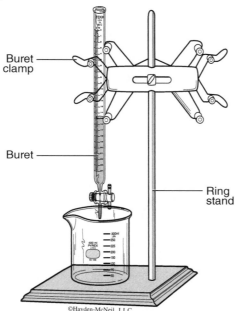

Buret clamp

Buret

Ring stand

©Hayden-McNeil, LLC

Figure C.4. Buret setup.

NOTES

Reading a Buret

Note that the numerical scale on a buret is set up to measure the amount of liquid delivered or drained—*NOT* the amount in the buret.

- After filling, wait a few seconds and then record the buret reading at the bottom of the meniscus. You may wish to use a 3 × 5 card with a black mark on it. Hold the black mark "behind" the buret so that it is just visible under the meniscus. This will darken the meniscus and make it easier to see against the white card.

- To avoid a parallax error, your eye must be level with the meniscus, and the buret vertical.

- The buret should be read to the nearest **0.01 mL**. Since the markings only occur every 0.1 mL, this requires estimating the reading to the nearest 0.01 mL.

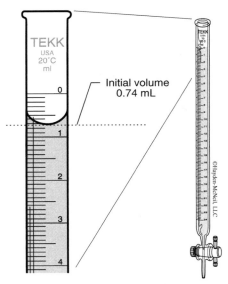

Figure C.5. Initial volume in the buret.

Titrating with a Buret

Although you may initially find it awkward, a right-handed person should use their left hand to operate the stopcock. To do this, wrap your left hand around the buret and move the stopcock by opposing pressure with your fingers and thumb. This leaves your dominant hand to swirl the flask. All titrating is done with the flask being swirled continuously to ensure the liquid added is well mixed with the solution in the flask.

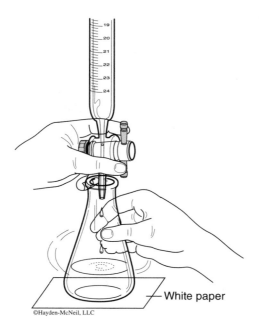

Figure C.6. Delivery of liquid from a buret.

Put the container into which liquid is to be dispensed under the buret tip and open the stopcock part way, permitting fluid to flow slowly into the container until the desired volume has been dispensed. Wait a few seconds and record the buret reading at the bottom of the meniscus. The volume dispensed is the difference between the final and initial buret readings.

Always perform a "scout" titration. The purpose is to roughly determine what volume of solution is required to reach the endpoint. To do this, open the stopcock so that the solution drains quickly into the flask. Close the stopcock as soon as you notice the color change. You will most likely miss the endpoint. Record the volume of the titrant in your notebook. Remember to subtract the initial buret volume.

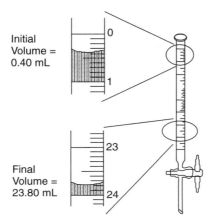

Figure C.7. Reading a buret.

NOTES

For a more careful titration, open the stopcock just as if you were performing a scout titration. However, stop 0.50 mL–1 mL before the volume expected for the endpoint. Now adjust the stopcock so the solution flows from the buret one drop at a time. An experienced analyst is capable of forming a fractional drop at the tip of the buret and transferring it to the flask by washing the tip with deionized water from a wash bottle or by tapping the flask against the tip. This is done often because one drop contains about 0.05 mL and the buret can be read to 0.01 mL.

If you are using an indicator for the first time and are not familiar with the color change, it might be wise to write down the volume the first time you think the color corresponds to the endpoint. Then add another drop to see how the color changes. If it looks more like the endpoint again, read the buret and write the volume in your notebook. Continue until you are convinced the endpoint has been reached or passed.

Sources of Error

Air bubbles—Air bubbles in the stopcock or buret tips will result in an error in the volume dispensed from the buret.

Improper cleaning—Drops of liquid or bubbles will form on the inside of the buret if the buret is contaminated with other reagents.

Parallax—Keep your eye level with the meniscus when reading the volume of the buret.

Over or underestimating the endpoint color—titration to an incorrect color.

Slow titration/stirring too vigorously/breathing into the flask—Some solutions are unstable and the titration must be performed quickly. Gases in the air such as carbon dioxide may react with the solution in your flask.

Cleanup

Clean the buret as soon as practical after using it with several rinses of DI water and return it to the proper location so it doesn't get broken. Burets are not cheap and you will have to pay for one if it breaks.

Volumetric Flasks

A special type of glassware called a volumetric flask is used to prepare accurate dilutions of standard and unknown solutions. The volumetric flask has a long thin neck with a calibration mark on it so that solutions can be diluted exactly to the mark.

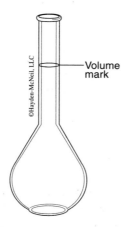

©Hayden-McNeil, LLC

Volume mark

Figure C.8. Volumetric flask.

Note that there may be three lines on the 50-mL plastic volumetric flasks. The middle line represents 50.0 mL.

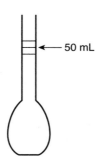

← 50 mL

Figure C.9. Plastic volumetric flask.

Before using a volumetric flask, wash with detergent solution and rinse several times with tap water, followed with a minimum of three deionized water rinses.

Make sure that all parts of the inside surface are rinsed.

After cleaning and rinsing, measure the aliquot of solution into it using pipets and burets as described previously. If instructions involve addition of one or more other reagents, then add those reagents at this time.

After all reagents have been added, add deionized water carefully from a clean dropper pipet or medicine dropper until the liquid meniscus is lined **exactly** with the calibration marking on the neck of the flask.

©Hayden-McNeil, LLC

Figure C.10. Filling a volumetric flask.

Volumetric flasks should be closed with Parafilm, thumb put over the Parafilm, and flask inverted for adequate mixing. Because the neck of the flask is long and narrow, several inversions are necessary to achieve good mixing.

©Hayden-McNeil, LLC

Figure C.11. Mixing liquid in a volumetric flask.

Mixing Solutions

Before you pour a small amount of solution into a small, clean, dry beaker to measure aliquots, always mix the solution thoroughly to ensure that any solvent that may have evaporated and condensed on the inside surface is remixed with the solution.

Dilution Factor

The **dilution factor** is the degree to which a sample has been diluted. For example, if we were to take a 25.00 mL sample of vinegar and dilute it to 1000 mL, the dilution factor would be 1000 mL/25 mL, corresponding to a 40-fold dilution of the vinegar sample. Stated differently, the concentration of acetic acid in the diluted sample would be one-fortieth (1/40) that of the original sample, or the original sample is 40 times more concentrated than the diluted sample.

Spectroscopy: An Introduction

D

Spectrophotometry is a method of chemical analysis based on measuring the amount of light absorbed by a substance. Molecules in the substance may absorb or transmit light differently at different wavelengths. The amount of light absorbed depends on the molecule involved and the concentration of these molecules, and can be used to determine the amount of a chemical substance. Spectrophotometry is a useful method of quantitative analysis in various fields such as chemistry, physics, biochemistry, pharmaceuticals, and clinical applications.

A spectrophotometer measures the percent of incident light a sample transmits, the percent transmission ($\%T$). The more light a sample absorbs, the smaller the percent transmission. The basic operating components of a spectrophotometer are diagrammed in Figure D.1, where P_0 is the intensity (brightness) of the light entering the cuvette. P is the intensity of the light that passes through the cuvette and sample, and is detected by the spectrophotometer. This is quantified as percent transmittance or $\%T = 100 \times (P / P_0)$.

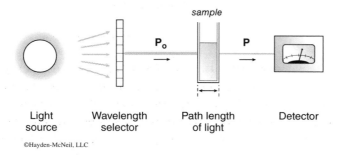

Figure D.1. Spectrophotometer schematic.

Another measure of light absorbed by a sample is the absorbance, A, where:

$$A = -\log \mathbf{P/P}_0 \text{ or } -\log (\%T/100).$$

NOTES

Absorbance is commonly used in spectroscopy because it is proportional to the concentration of the absorbing molecule. The absorbance is also proportional to the path length of light through the sample. The relationship between absorbance at a given wavelength and concentration and path length can be expressed as:

$$\text{absorbance} = (\text{molar absorptivity}) \times \left(\begin{array}{c} \text{path length of light} \\ \text{through the sample} \end{array} \right) \times (\text{concentration})$$

$$A \quad = \quad \varepsilon \quad \times \quad \ell \quad \times \quad C$$

This relationship is known as the Beer-Lambert Law. The molar absorptivity, ε, is a measure of how strongly a chemical substance absorbs light at a given wavelength, and is an intrinsic property of the substance.

Absorption Spectra and Finding the Wavelength of Maximum Absorption

The plot of a compound's absorbance of light at various wavelengths is called its **absorption spectrum** (horizontal axis = wavelength, vertical axis = absorbance). The graph shown gives the absorption spectrum of yellow, red, and blue food dyes.

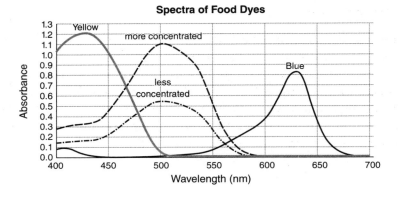

Figure D.2. Absorption spectra of some food dyes.

For quantitative measurements, it is preferable to choose a wavelength of light that is near the maximum absorbance, λ_{max}, for the compound of interest. For example, the λ_{max} for red dye is approximately 500 nm. The choice of wavelength for making absorbance measurements is important, and there are two reasons we generally select the wavelength of maximum absorbance (λ_{max}) for a given compound and use it for absorbance measurements.

1. It is where the change in absorbance is greatest for a change in concentration. That is, the measurement of absorbance (concentration) is most sensitive at this wavelength.

2. It is where the change in absorbance is least for a slight change in the wavelength. That is, the absorbance will be less sensitive to any error in the spectrophotometer selection of the wavelength. Suppose that a wavelength of 550 nm was chosen for the measurement of red food dye. This measurement is on the steep portion of the curve, where a small change in the wavelength would cause a large change in the absorbance. Using the wavelength maximum of 500 nm, which has a relatively flat profile, will minimize the error in the absorbance if there is a slight error in the wavelength.

Limits of Spectrophotometers

A spectrophotometer has limitations in the maximum absorbance it can measure accurately, so the concentration of the solutions must be chosen so the absorbance measurements are within the linear or working range of the instrument (typically less than 1.5).

The following graph illustrates absorbance data obtained over a wide range of concentrations. As the concentration increases, the measured absorbance levels off because the amount of light transmitted through the sample is now so small that the instrument can no longer detect any difference in absorbance. The region of concentrations chosen for the standard solutions and samples must be below the point where the curve deviates from a straight line. If a sample concentration is outside this range, it must be diluted until the concentration is within the range of the standard concentrations.

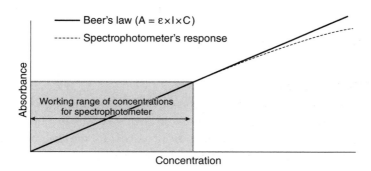

Figure D.3. Linear or working range of the spectrophotometer.

Standard Curves

The molar absorptivity of a molecule can vary as a function of wavelength, temperature, solvent, pH, and other chemical conditions, so if the conditions of your sample don't match those with which the molar absorptivity was determined, the calculated concentration won't be accurate. Also, spectrometers are not identical and may not necessarily give identical results or even the same results on different days. A **standard curve** is a necessary part of determining the concentrations of substances using spectroscopy. A standard curve is a graph of known data (absorbance vs. concentration) that is used to determine the unknown concentration of a substance in a solution. Several solutions are prepared with known concentrations of the substance of interest and are called **standards** or **standard solutions** and are the independent variable. The measured property, absorbance at a selected wavelength, is the dependent variable.

Molar absorptivity, ε, is a proportionality constant and is an intrinsic property of a species. Therefore, in a graph of absorbance vs. concentration of standard solutions, the slope of the best-fit line or trendline is equal to the molar absorptivity of that substance at a given wavelength and path length of light through the sample (see Figure D.4).

When you know the molar absorptivity of the substance of interest and the absorbance of the solution, you can calculate the concentration of the substance of interest in the solution.

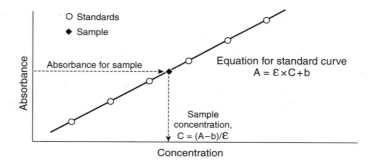

Figure D.4. Interpreting a standard curve: absorbance vs. concentration.

The Blank Solution

The solvent, cuvette material, or solutes other than the compound of interest may also absorb light. These interferences can be corrected for by filling a cuvette with a solution containing all the components except for the absorbing species of interest. This is referred to as a **blank solution**. Setting the spectrophotometer to "0" absorbance with the blank solution instructs the instrument to subtract the absorbance due to blank from the absorbance of future samples. An analogy is the taring of a balance to subtract the weight of the empty container.

Summary

Measurement and analysis procedures of spectrometry include:

1. Determination of an appropriate wavelength to make absorbance measurements

2. Measurement of absorbance of standards using a spectrophotometer

3. Construction of a standard curve (absorbance vs. concentration):

    a. to obtain the equation of the best-fit straight line through the data points

    b. to obtain the molar absorptivity from the equation of the line

4. Measure absorbance of unknown solution and use standard curve to determination its concentration

Cuvettes

Cuvettes hold the sample that is to be inserted into a spectrophotometer for measurement. Cuvettes may be made of plastic or glass and may be rectangular or cylindrical. Glass cuvettes are **NOT** test tubes. Cuvettes are manufactured more carefully for optical clarity than test tubes and are, therefore, more expensive. To make measurements of solutions accurately, the following procedures need to be followed.

- Handle cuvettes with care to avoid scratching or damaging them. Never use a test tube brush to clean a cuvette. (*Scratches scatter light!*)

- Use the same cuvette for all measurements unless you have a set of precisely matched cuvettes.

- Rinse the cuvette first with deionized water and then twice with a small amount (~1 mL) of solution that is to be measured. "Roll" the solution in the cuvette so all the inside surface is rinsed. Empty all rinses into a beaker that is being used as a waste container.

- Start measurements with the lowest concentration, then progress to the highest concentration. Empty the solution from the cuvette into the waste container, rinse with the next more concentrated solution, and then fill cuvette with solution.

- Plastic cuvettes need to be about ¾ full for measurements. Glass cuvettes need to be about ½ full.

- Make sure there are no bubbles in the solution to be measured. (*Bubbles refract light!*)

- Clean the outside of the cuvette with an absorbent, lint-free, soft tissue such as Kimwipes. (*Fingerprints absorb and scatter light!*)

- Insert the cuvette into the sample compartment or sample holder the same way each time. Most cuvettes have a mark to help orient it the same way each time.

Using the Vernier SpectroVis Plus™ Spectrophotometer

Figure D.5. The Vernier SpectroVis Plus™ spectrophotometer.

You must pay attention to the orientation of the cuvettes in a spectrophotometer. Some cuvettes are clear on all sides and require no particular orientation. However, reduced volume cuvettes and cuvettes with textured or frosted sides must be inserted into the SpectroVis so that the light passes through the sample without deflection.

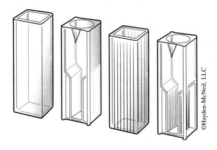

Figure D.6. Examples of different types of cuvettes.

Note the figure below showing the sample holder of the SpectroVis Plus. The source light originates from the right side of the instrument and is detected on the left. You must insert the cuvette in the spectrophotometer so that the light will pass through the clear sides of the cuvette.

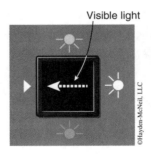

Figure D.7. Direction of light path through the sample compartment of the SpectroVis Plus.

Connect the SpectroVis Plus to the Computer

- Turn on the computer; log on to your account.

- Connect the SpectroVis spectrophotometer to the computer with a USB cable.

- Start the Logger *Pro* application by clicking on the Logger *Pro* icon on the desktop.

Set the SpectroVis Plus to Zero

- Prepare a blank solution.

- Fill a cuvette about ¾ full with the blank solution.

- From the **Experiment** menu, choose **Calibrate > Spectrophotometer:1.**

- Wait. The Calibrate Spec window will pop up and count down time for the lamp to warm up.

- Place the cuvette with the blank in the sample chamber of the SpectroVis.

- Click **Finish Calibration.**

- Click **OK.**

Collecting a Spectrum (Absorbance vs. Wavelength) to Find the Wavelength of Maximum Absorbance

- Click on the **Configure Spectrometer** button, 🔦, also known as "Rainbow Mtn."

- Select **Absorbance vs. Wavelength** as the Collection Mode.

- Fill a cuvette about ¾ full with one of the standards.

- Place the cuvette in the sample chamber of the SpectroVis.

- Click ▶ **Collect** .

- Wait 10 seconds.

- Click ■ **Stop** to end data collection.

- Press **Autoscale**, 📊 , for a better representation of the spectra.

Collecting Data for a Standard Curve (Absorbance vs. Concentration)

- Click on **Configure Spectrometer,** 🔦.

- Select **Absorbance vs. Concentration** as the Collection Mode. **NOTE: Logger *Pro* has chosen the wavelength of maximum absorbance, λ_{max}, for you.**

- Change the **Column Name** to Concentration, the **Short Name** to conc, and the **Units** to M or mol/L.

- Click **OK.**

- Measure the standards from the least concentrated to the most concentrated:

  1. Rinse the cuvette with a small amount of the standard solution by rolling the solution in the cuvette. Discard the rinse into a waste beaker.

2. Fill the cuvette about ¾ full with the standard solution.

3. Insert the cuvette into the spectrophotometer. Press **Collect**.

4. Wait 10 seconds, then press ⊗ **keep** . Enter the concentration. NOTE: A value in scientific notation such as 1.00×10^{-3} must be entered as 1.00E-3. Press **OK**.

5. Repeat with other standards.

• Click **Stop** to end data collection.

Collecting Data for Kinetics (Absorbance vs. Time)

• Click on **Configure Spectrometer**, ⬛.

• Select **Absorbance vs. Time** as the Collection Mode. Change the **Column Name** to Concentration, the **Short Name** to conc, and the **Units** to M or mol/L.

• Click **OK**.

• Click **Collect**. Observe the progress of the reaction. Click **Stop** to end the data collection.

Filtration

Filtration is a technique used for two main purposes. The first is to remove solid impurities from a liquid. The second is to collect a desired solid from a solution where it was precipitated or crystallized. The two general filtration methods are gravity filtration and vacuum filtration.

Gravity filtration uses gravity to draw a solution through a paper filter held in a funnel. It is often used to remove solid impurities from a solution.

©Hayden-McNeil, LLC

To perform a gravity filtration:

1. Rest the funnel in a triangle supported by a ring on a ring stand, and set a beaker underneath the funnel.

2. Fold the filter paper in half, and then in half again, as shown. Open the filter paper into a cone, place the filter paper cone in the funnel, and moisten the paper with a few milliliters of the solvent used (usually water). The moistened filter paper should help keep it in place for the filtration. Allow the solvent to pass through the filter paper into the beaker. Once the solvent has stopped draining through the funnel, replace the beaker with a clean one to collect the filtrate.

3. Before filtering, allow the solid in the mixture to settle to the bottom of the container. Carefully pour the liquid into the center of the funnel, being careful not to let the level of liquid rise above the top edge of the filter paper. By initially transferring only the liquid portion of the mixture, the filtration will take less time.

4. Once most of the liquid has passed through the filter, transfer the solid from the container into the funnel. Swirl a few milliliters of solvent with the solid that remains in the original container and quickly (while the solid is still suspended) transfer this mixture to the filtration funnel. Repeat with small portions of solvent until all the solid is transferred to the filter. The volume of the rinses should be minimal so that it does not dissolve too much of the solid or dilute the filtrate too much.

5. Washing the solid is important, whether the solid or filtrate will be collected. If the solid is to be collected, washing will remove any soluble impurities. If the filtrate is to be collected, washing will ensure that all of the solute (the compound that you want that is dissolved in the solvent) is removed from the solid and collected in the filtrate. The volume of the washes should be minimal so that it does not dissolve too much of the solid or dilute the filtrate too much.

Vacuum filtration uses a vacuum to draw a solution through a paper filter. Vacuum filtration is faster than gravity filtration because the solution is forced through the filter paper by a pressure difference. It is often used to collect solid products resulting from precipitation or crystallization.

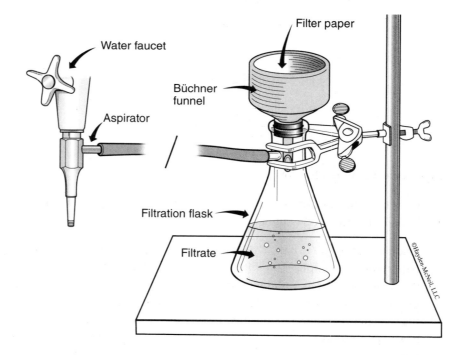

To perform a vacuum filtration:

1. Obtain a filter flask, Büchner funnel, rubber funnel adapter, bucket, and thick-walled tubing from the drawers or cabinets in the back of the laboratory. Clamp the filter flask securely to a ring stand with a 3-prong clamp.

2. Connect the rubber tubing to the flask and aspirator. Place a bucket under the aspirator and fill the bucket with water. This helps reduce the splashing when the aspirator water flow is turned on full.

3. Insert a Büchner funnel into the top of the filter flask with a rubber funnel adaptor. Wetting the adaptor can help make the seal airtight.

4. Place the filter paper in the funnel. The filter paper should be small enough to remain flat but large enough to cover all of the holes in the funnel. Wet the filter paper with a small amount of the solvent to be used in the filtration. This will help the filter paper adhere to the bottom and keep solids from passing under the paper during filtration.

5. Turn on the water for the aspirator. The vacuum generated by the aspirator should draw the wet filter paper against the bottom of the funnel, sealing the bottom. You might need to lightly press down on the funnel to help seal around the rubber filter adaptor.

6. Pour the mixture into the center of the filter paper. The vacuum should rapidly pull the liquid through the funnel. Keep the accumulating solid in the center of the filter paper to minimize the chances of the liquid and solid bypassing the filter paper. Rinse the filter cake with a small amount of fresh, cold solvent to help remove impurities that were in the solution.

7. Continue to run the aspirator. This will draw some air through the solid, which helps to dry it somewhat.

8. Disconnect the rubber tubing from the flask before turning off the water flow to the aspirator. If the water in the aspirator stops flowing with the tubing still attached to the filter flask, the reduced pressure inside the flask may draw water from inside the aspirator into the filter flask.

NOTES

CHAPTER 1

Laboratory Basics

This laboratory project is designed to help you gain experience with certain techniques used in this course. The experiments in this course will require that you are able to use **volumetric glassware** and **micropipets** (sometimes referred to as pipetters) to accurately measure solutions. You will also be required to use instrumentation such as a **spectrophotometer** to measure prepared solutions. Finally, you will be required to present measured data graphically and interpret your data.

Today, you will learn how to use some common laboratory volumetric glassware and a micropipet. With these tools you will prepare serial dilutions of a food dye solution. You will measure the concentration of the diluted food dye samples using a spectrophotometer, then create graphical representations of your data with Excel.

There is an inherent precision associated with each piece of glassware used in the laboratory. This precision is expressed as an uncertainty in the measured value and affects the number of significant digits reported in a given measurement.

In the table below, we have listed the uncertainty or tolerance of the glassware that you will use in this laboratory exercise and other experiments throughout the semester.

Table 1.1. Tolerances for Volumetric Glassware and the Micropipet.

Volume or Volume Range	Tolerance	Volume or Volume Range	Tolerance
Measuring pipet		Volumetric flask	
5 mL	± 0.02 mL	25 mL	± 0.03 mL
		50 mL	± 0.05 mL
		100 mL	± 0.08 mL
Transfer pipet		Micropipet or pipetter	
10 mL	± 0.02 mL	20–200 µL	± 0.60 µL
25 mL	± 0.03 mL	100–1000 µL	± 0.60 µL

Each member of your group should take this opportunity to practice using the pipets and the spectrophotometer. Please divide the work so that each member can practice using the volumetric glassware and instrumentation. Each student in the group is to take responsibility for the data collection and data analysis.

Prelab

Before coming to lab, please read How to Be Successful in CHM 12901: A Guide to Using Laboratory Equipment and Instrumentation as well as the section in your textbook describing serial dilution and the handout describing how to use a pipettor. Complete the Excel exercise. You are to turn in your formatted sheet, charts, and Word document to your teaching assistant. The information in the sheet, charts, and on the document must show that you have completed all the steps in the Basics of Excel exercise.

Prelab Exercise: The Basics of Excel®

The instructions below were written for the 2016 version of Excel. If you are using a different version of the program, the steps necessary to complete the exercise may be slightly different.

Open Excel and choose a Blank workbook. A grid will appear. Rows will be numbered and columns will be labeled with letters.

Part I. Data Entry and Simple Spreadsheet Formulas

A. Calculations

1. Enter the X and Y data from Table 1.2 Absorbance versus Concentration of $KMnO_4$: x-variable (Concentration of $KMnO_4$) in column A, y-variable (Absorbance) in column B. Use row 1 for column labels. The data represents the amount of light absorbed by increasing concentrations of a colored compound, potassium permanganate, $KMnO_4$, in solution. In this hypothetical data set, the concentration of $KMnO_4$ is the independent variable, X, and the value of the response (absorbance) of the instrument measuring the light is the dependent variable, Y. The independent variable, concentration, drives the value of the dependent variable, absorbance. Note that Absorbance does not have units.

   It is convention when titling a graph to name the dependent, Y, value first then the independent variable, X. For example, a graph of the data in the table would have the title, Absorbance versus Concentration of $KMnO_4$ (M).

Table 1.2. Absorbance (at 510 nm) versus Concentration of $KMnO_4$ (M).

Concentration of $KMnO_4$ (M)	Absorbance (510 nm)
0.0300	0.162
0.0600	0.330
0.0900	0.499
0.120	0.670

2. Calculate functions of the y-variable that you will graph. Program column C to calculate 1/Absorbance for each value of Absorbance in column B.

   a. Place the cursor over cell C2 and click. A rectangle will appear at the top of the columns. This is where you can view what information is in each cell.

   b. Type the following exactly as it appears. The equal sign is very important because this is the symbol that tells the spreadsheet that the information that follows is a formula and that it should compute the value for the selected cell.

   =1/B2

   Press the ENTER key and the answer will appear in cell C2.

Common symbols used for programming the spreadsheet for calculations:

The ^ symbol in a formula means "raised to the power of…"

The * symbol means "multiply by."

The + symbol means "add"; – means "subtract."

The "/" symbol means "divide by."

"LOG10" means "take the logarithm, base 10, of…"

"LN" means "take the natural logarithm of…"

"SQRT" is used to calculate a square root.

"B2:B5" represents the range of cells B2 through B5.

---

   c. Next select the cells C2 down to C5. Do this by putting the cursor over C2, hold down the left mouse button and drag the pointer to the last row of your data. When you release the mouse, the cells in column C that you selected should be shaded.

   d. On the **HOME** tab, in the **Edit** group, click **FILL** then **DOWN**. The result of the computation in each row will appear.

> The order in which mathematical operations are executed in Excel is:
>
> range (:), before negation on an operand (e.g., $10^\wedge-7$), before exponentiation ($\wedge$), before multiplication and division ($*$ and $/$), before addition and subtraction (+ and –). The best way to avoid errors is to use parentheses to force the various operations to be executed in the order you wish, as is done with an inner set of parentheses. For example, "3+4*5" would give 23 whereas "(3+4)5" would give 35.

3. Before going further, program column D to calculate the base 10 logarithm of Absorbance, column E to calculate the square root of Absorbance, and column F to calculate Absorbance^2. Check your work by performing the calculations with your calculator. Label the columns.

B. Format the Spreadsheet

1. Change the column width by putting the cursor on the line that separates column A from column B. The shape of the cursor will change. Holding the left mouse button down, drag the cursor left and right to change the column width.

2. **Toolbar Functions**

   a. Look at your X and Y data in Table 1.2. How many significant figures are in each value? Now adjust the values in each column to reflect the number of significant digits in each value. Select the cells containing numbers where decimal points are to be adjusted. Click the **increase or decrease decimal point** icon (in the **Number** group of the **HOME** tab) until the columns have the appropriate number of significant figures.

   b. Select the column headers in row 1 and position them in the center of the column by clicking the **Center** icon (in the **Alignment** group of the **HOME** tab).

   c. Click on the **Page Layout** tab, and then click on the **Print Titles** icon in the **Page Setup** group.

   When the **Page Setup** window is displayed, click on the **Header/Footer** tab.

   i. Click on **Custom Header**. Click in the box labeled **Left section** and type (on two separate lines) your names and your lab section number.

   Click in the box labeled **Center section** and type The Basics of Excel.

   Click in the box **Right section** and type in today's date and time.

   Click **OK**.

   ii. While still in **Page Setup**, click on the **Sheet** tab, then click the box labeled **Gridlines,** then click OK.

Part II. Graphing x-y Data, Computing Trendlines, and R-Squared Values

A. Plotting an x-y Data Set and a Trendline

1. **Plotting the Data Points**

   a. Select the data to be plotted as follows: Place the cursor over the first data point to be plotted on the x-axis (concentration of $KMnO_4$), click and hold the left mouse button, and drag the mouse to the bottom of the column of numbers. The column should be highlighted. Release the mouse button.

      While pressing the **Control** (CTRL) key, place the cursor over the first data point to be plotted on the y-axis (absorbance), click, hold, and drag the mouse to select the values in that column to be plotted. Release the **Control** key and the mouse button. Now two columns should be highlighted.

      Depending on which version of Excel you are using, the order of completing the next steps may vary but essentially you need to do the following as you work through this exercise.

   b. Under the **Charts** group in the **Insert** tab, choose the **Scatter** (X,Y) chart type. Choose the icon that shows data points only (no lines).

   c. Click on the chart. The **Chart Tools** menu will be displayed at the top of the screen. Click on **Add Chart Elements** in the **Chart Layout** group, add chart and axis titles, and rename the chart. Normally, you must always include units in your axes and chart titles. Absorbance values are an exception. Absorbance is unitless.

   d. To move the chart to a separate sheet, right-click on the chart (but off the graph) and select **Move Chart**, then select **New sheet** or an existing sheet.

2. **Displaying the Trendline and R-Squared Value on the Graph**

Best-fit line or trendline is used to graphically display the relationship or correlation between variables. A linear trendline has an equation of the form $y = mx + b$. The slope of the line is m and b is the y-intercept. The equation is useful in predicting the value of one variable based on established values.

The correlation coefficient or R^2 value associated with a trendline is a measure of the linear correlation between the two variables x and y. This value is a number from 0 to 1. An R^2 value of 1 implies that the equation for the trendline describes the relationship between x and y perfectly with all data points lying on the trendline.

   a. Move the mouse cursor to any data point on the chart and press the left mouse button. All of the data points should now be highlighted. Now, while the mouse cursor is still on any one of the highlighted data points, press and hold the right mouse button, and choose **Add Trendline** from the menu that appears. Click on the box with the type of fit you want (e.g., Linear). Select **Linear**, **Display Equation on chart** and **Display R-squared on the chart**.

B. Adding a Second Data Set to an Existing Graph

1. Using the procedure outlined below, add 1/Absorbance vs. Concentration of $KMnO_4$ (M) to the graph.

2. Go back to the sheet containing the original data by clicking the sheet tab along the bottom of the Excel window.

   a. Place the cursor over the first data point to be plotted on the *x-axis*, click and hold the left mouse button, and drag the mouse to the bottom of the column. The column should be highlighted. Release the mouse button.

      While pressing the **Control** key, place the cursor over the first data point to be plotted on the *y-axis*, click, hold, and drag the mouse to select the values in that column to be plotted. Release the Control key and the mouse button. Now the two columns should be highlighted.

   b. Under the **HOME** tab, select **Copy**. Click on the chart where the new data is to be placed.

      Under the **Paste** icon in the **HOME** tab, select **Paste Special**, then select **New series** and **Categories (X Values) in First Column**. Click OK.

   c. Insert a trendline and its equation following the same procedures as described previously.

3. Save the Excel workbook.

4. Print the worksheet and chart by choosing **Print** from the **File** menu.

Part III. Transferring Tables and Graphs to a Word Document

A. Transfer and Format the Spreadsheet/Table

1. Open **Word** and choose a blank document.

2. Return to the Excel program. Click the **Sheet** tab at the bottom, then select or highlight all the cells that contain your data.

   From the **Clipboard** group in the **HOME** tab, click **Copy**.

3. Return to your Word document, place the cursor on the page, and from the **Clipboard** group in the **HOME** tab, click **Paste**.

4. Select/highlight all transferred data. In the **Paragraph** group in the **HOME** tab, select **All Borders** under the **Border** icon.

B. Transfer and Format the Graph/Chart

1. Return to Excel, click **Chart 1**. Click toward the outer edge of the chart. A thick border with dotted corners and edges should surround your entire graph. From the **Clipboard** group in the **HOME** tab, click **Copy**.

2. Return to your Word document. Place the cursor below the table you copied and pasted previously. From the **Clipboard** group in the **HOME** tab, click **Paste**.

3. To change the position of the graph/chart on the page, first select the Layout Options icon beside the chart and change to Wrap Text Top and Bottom. Place the cursor over the graph, right-click, hold, and drag the graph.

   To change the size of the graph/chart on the page, place the cursor over the graph and right-click. Position the cursor over any of the dotted edges or corners around the graph, left-click, hold, and drag the mouse until the desired size is obtained.

Select **Print** from the **File** menu and print your Word document.

Safety

WEAR your goggles. Goggles must remain on until you leave the lab.

Procedure

Lab work is performed in groups of four students. Each person must record a complete set of data for each dilution series in his/her lab notebook and turn in the duplicate copy on the perforated pages at the end of lab.

Materials

From your lab drawer

- Medicine droppers
- Wash bottle of deionized water
- Test tube support
- 4–100-mL beakers (clean and dry)

From the box of equipment on your bench

- SpectroVis Plus spectrophotometer
- USB–USB-B connector
- Power adapter
- Wooden block

From your graduate instructor

- 10- and 25-mL pipets
- 6–disposable, plastic cuvettes

From the back of the lab room

- 50- and 100-mL volumetric flasks
- Pipet bulb

From the shelf beside the front sink

- Kimwipes (lint-free tissue)
- Parafilm

From the reagent bench

- 20 mL red food dye (25.0 mM)

From the balance room

- 200-µL and 1000-µL pipetters

Your group will perform two serial dilutions of red food dye: a macro scale dilution in volumetric flasks and a micro scale dilution performed directly in the cuvettes.

Macro Scale Serial Dilution

Using water, food dye, and volumetric pipets, prepare a serial dilution of red food dye using the scheme pictured in Figure 1.1. Obtain 20 mL of red dye. Begin by transferring the appropriate amount of food dye into a 100-mL volumetric flask then fill the flask with deionized water to the appropriate mark. Remember to mix the diluted solutions completely before transferring aliquots. Mix each dilution by stretching a small piece of Parafilm over the opening of the flask; press a finger or thumb firmly over the opening and invert at least three times. Pour the diluted solutions into a small beaker after mixing. Do not try to pipet samples from the volumetric flasks. Between each dilution, rinse the pipet with a small amount of the solution that you will transfer.

**❚ Please Note: the 50-mL plastic volumetric flasks have three calibration
■ marks or lines. The middle line represents 50.0 mL. See page xxxiii–
xxxiv for proper use of volumetric flasks.**

NOTES

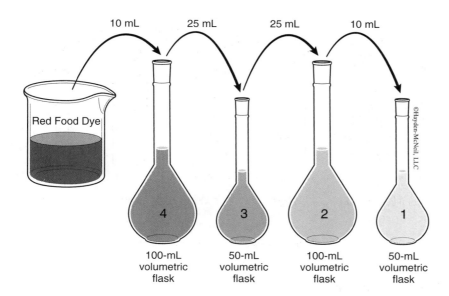

Figure 1.1. Macro scale serial dilution.

Micro Scale Serial Dilution

This time you will prepare the dilutions directly in the cuvette that you will use to measure concentration. Each dilution will have a total volume of 2 mL (2000 μL). Using water, food dye, and a micropipet prepare a serial dilution of red food dye using the scheme below. Begin by transferring the appropriate amount of deionized water into each cuvette.

Attach a pipet tip to the 1000-μL pipetter. Dispense the amount of water shown in Figure 1.2. You may use the same pipet tip to dispense water into all the samples. Discard the tip.

Attach a new tip to the 200-μL pipetter.

Add 100 μL of red food dye to cuvette 4. Mix the sample by slowly and carefully pulling the solution into the pipet tip then dispensing the solution back into the cuvette. Repeat at least three times. Discard the tip. Remember to mix the diluted solutions completely before transferring aliquots. Next, attach a new tip to the 1000-μL pipetter and transfer 1000 μL of the solution from cuvette 4 to 3 and mix as described above. Continue with dilution as pictured in Figure 1.2.

NOTES

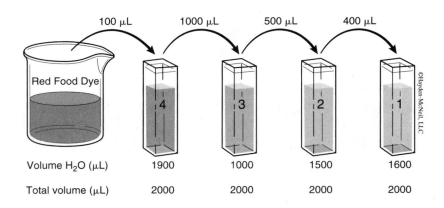

Figure 1.2. Micro scale serial dilution.

Data Collection

Connect the SpectroVis Plus to the LabQuest 2
! **THE FOLLOWING STEPS MUST BE PERFORMED IN ORDER.**

USB-A connect
to LabQuest

USB-B connect
to SpectroVis

1. Connect the power adapter to the LabQuest, and plug it in. Insert the USB-A into the LabQuest.

2. Turn on the LabQuest and wait for the **Meter** screen to appear.

3. Connect the USB-B end of the cable to the SpectroVis.

4. The LabQuest screen will display **USB: Abs**.

Set the Vernier SpectroVis Plus to Zero Absorbance
Before the dye can be measured, it is necessary to obtain an absorption scan for the blank solution. An absorption scan of the blank is used to correct for any absorbance of light by the solvent, impurities or irregularities in the optics of the instrument. When you zero the spectrometer, the absorbance of the blank solution will be measured over the entire wavelength range. The resulting Absorbance versus Wavelength data will be stored internally. When the absorbance of a sample (such as red dye) is subsequently measured, the absorption scan of the blank solution will be used as an internal reference. The instrument sets itself internally to use the blank measurement as 0 absorbance; in other words 100% of the light passes through the blank.

1. From the **Sensors** menu, choose **Calibrate > USB: Spectrometer**. The calibration dialog box will display the message: "Taking dark sample" then "Waiting 90 seconds for lamp to warm up."

2. When warmup is complete, rinse and fill a cuvette with deionized water (the blank solution). Wipe the outside of the blank with a Kimwipe and insert in the spectrophotometer.

3. Click **Finish Calibration** then **OK**.

4. Save the blank in case you need to recalibrate the spectrometer.

Set the Wavelength of the Spectrophotometer

1. Rinse another cuvette with **macro scale solution 1** and fill the cuvette at least ¾ full with this standard solution.

2. Wipe the outside of the cuvette with a Kimwipe and insert it into the spectrometer.

3. Tap on the **green arrow** to start data collection. You will see a graph of the spectrum for red food dye.

4. Wait a few seconds. Tap on the **red square** to stop data collection.

5. Move the cursor along the graph to choose the maximum absorbance for the dye. The wavelength and absorbance will be displayed to the right of the graph. The maximum should be near 500 nm. Record the maximum wavelength, concentration and absorbance of solution 1 in your notebook.

6. Now set the collection mode, by tapping the meter icon, .

7. Tap on the grey **Mode** box. Tap on **Mode** and choose **Time Based**.

8. Click **OK** and **Discard** the spectrum data.

Now that the parameters are set for the LabQuest and spectrometer, all you need to do to measure absorbance of a sample is to insert the sample into the spectrometer.

You should have recorded the absorbance of solution 1 and can now continue with the remaining macro scale solutions from the least concentrated (2) to the most concentrated (4):

1. Discard solution 1 and rinse the same cuvette with solution 2.

2. Fill the cuvette ¾ full with solution 2 and wipe the outside of the cuvette with a Kimwipe.

3. Insert the cuvette into the spectrophotometer.

4. Wait a few seconds and record the absorbance displayed.

5. Record the concentration and absorbance of the solution in your lab notebook.

6.   Repeat steps 1–5 with the other macro scale standard solutions.

7.   **Insert wooden block into the spectrometer.** Since you have prepared the micro scale solutions in cuvettes, all you need to do is wipe the outside of the cuvettes with a Kimwipe and insert the cuvettes into the spectrometer. Repeat steps 3–5 with the micro scale standard solutions.

8.   Discard the solutions and cuvettes.

Transfer the Macro and Micro Scale Solution Data to an Excel File

Open Excel. Label column A: Concentration of Red Food Dye (mM); and column B: Absorbance. Enter your data from the measurement of the macro scale solutions into the appropriate columns. Rename Sheet1; Macro Scale.

Add a new sheet to your workbook. Label column A: Concentration of Red Food Dye (mM); and column B: Absorbance. Enter your data from the measurement of the micro scale solutions into the appropriate columns. Rename Sheet1; Micro Scale.

Save the data.

Cleanup and Waste Disposal

All solutions may be discarded down the sink followed by a good amount of water.

Plastic cuvettes and pipet tips are ONE-use plasticware. They must be disposed of in the trash.

Return all equipment to its proper location.

Shut down the LabQuest by tapping the **Home** icon then **System** > **Shut down**. Return the spectrometer, USB connector, wooden block, LabQuest, and power adapter to the box on your bench.

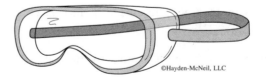

©Hayden-McNeil, LLC

Keep your splash goggles on over your eyes as you complete the lab report. Do not take off your splash goggles until you are ready to leave lab. Do not take them off or put them on your forehead and stand around talking to your group members. If you have your goggles off, then wait in the hallway to meet your group members or others after they leave the lab.

Data Analysis

Prepare separate graphs for the two types of serial dilutions. Display the trend-lines and R^2 values for each type of dilution on the graphs.

Your group is to prepare a report in Microsoft Word including:

- Title
- Lab group members' names
- A goal statement
- Procedural reference (lab manual title and page numbers)
- The data section should include a formatted data sheet that has been transferred from the Excel file into Word.
- The data analysis section should include imported graphs from Excel. Resize the graphs so that each occupy about ½ of a sheet of paper.
- Your printed report is due at the beginning of the next scheduled lab period.

Postlab Questions

1. Using Excel, construct a graph of absorbance vs. concentration for both the macro scale and micro scale serial dilutions. Be sure to label your axes (including units) and display the equations and R^2 values for the trendlines.

2. Describe the relationship between absorbance and concentration of the solutions based on the graphs you made of your data.

3. Why is it important to set the wavelength of the spectrophotometer before measuring the absorbance of the solutions?

4. What is the purpose of making a standard curve?

5. Describe how you could use the standard curve to help you determine the concentration of an unknown solution of red dye in the lab.

NOTES

CHAPTER 2

Iron Deficiency Analysis 2

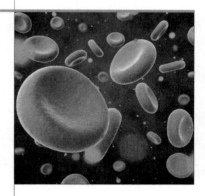

Introduction

An important aspect of chemistry is the development of standard procedures for the screening and detection of elements and compounds in biological systems. Analytical chemists devise analytical methods for quantifying the levels of minerals in the blood, tissue, water supplies, and food sources.

Standard procedures and methods have been developed for the analysis of iron deficiency in humans. These methods are useful in the diagnosis and treatment of disorders relating to iron intake, absorption, storage, and release mechanisms. Such changes are indicative of a wide range of dysfunctions including anemias, nephrosis, cirrhosis, and hepatitis.

In this experiment, you will be using a standard analytical method for detection of serum iron concentrations. In the clinical procedure, the test solution—be it serum or whole blood from a patient—is treated with a chemical reducing agent, then a chelating agent known as FerroZine™ which forms several bonds to the iron cation, Fe^{2+}. The Fe^{2+}–FerroZine™ complex forms a highly colored solution that can be quantified with a spectrophotometer.

It is not enough to measure the iron level in the serum. Clinicians must perform three tests:

- **Serum iron.** This colorimetric test using FerroZine™ measures the amount of free iron in your blood. The level of iron in your blood may be normal even if the total amount of iron in your body is low. For this reason, other iron tests are also performed.

- **Serum ferritin.** Ferritin is a protein that stores iron in your tissues and releases it when iron is needed. The ferritin protein also protects the cells from the free iron cation, which is toxic to the cells. The ferritin protein is detected and quantified by immunoassay. A measure of this protein in blood helps your doctor find out how much of your body's stored iron has been used.

- **Transferrin level, or total iron-binding capacity.** Transferrin is another protein that carries iron in your blood. Total iron-binding capacity measures how much of the transferrin is not bound to iron. For this test, an excess of iron is added to the serum sample to saturate the transferrin protein. The free iron (not bound to transferrin) is then quantified colorimetrically by adding FerroZine™ to the sample. This quantity of free iron is subtracted from the amount of iron added to the sample to find the maximum amount of iron the sample can carry, hence the level of transferrin in the sample. If you have iron-deficiency anemia, you'll have a high level of transferrin that is not bound to iron.

The normal serum iron concentration in humans falls within a range depending on sex and age. Please note that the units of iron concentration are micrograms per deciliter.

	Iron Concentration (µg/dL)
Adult Male	70–175
Adult Female	30–175
Children	50–120

You will not be performing these tests on human blood or serum; instead you will be mimicking the serum iron test by determining the amount of iron in a simulated serum sample.

Your group's objectives for this experiment are to:

- Prepare standard Fe^{2+} solutions from ammonium Iron(II) sulfate hexahydrate solid.

- Construct a standard curve for Fe^{2+}.

- Use the Fe^{2+} standard curve to find the concentration of iron in a simulated serum sample.

How Does the Assay Work?

The compound used in the screening is 3-(2-Pyridyl)-5,6-diphenyl-1,2,4-triazine-p,p'-disulfonic acid monosodium salt; commonly known as FerroZine™. FerroZine™ is colorless in solution. When iron(II), Fe^{2+}, is present the two species form a complex that is a purple in color. The intensity of the color is directly related to the concentration of Fe^{2+} present.

$$Fe^{2+}(aq) + 3\ (FerroZine)^{2-}(aq) \rightarrow Fe\ (FerroZine)_3^{4-}$$
$$\text{colorless} \qquad\qquad \text{purple}$$

The formation of a colored complex allows easy detection and quantification with a spectrophotometer.

The FerroZine™ reagent only binds to iron in the +2 oxidation state, so a reducing agent must also be added to the assay to reduce any Fe^{3+} present in the sample. You will add the reducing agent hydroxylamine hydrochloride, $NH_2OH \cdot HCl$, to reduce Fe^{3+} to Fe^{2+} as shown in the following reaction.

$$4\ Fe^{3+} + 2\ NH_2OH \rightarrow 4\ Fe^{2+} + N_2O + 4\ H^+ + H_2O$$

In this experiment, you will first make a standard stock solution of Fe^{2+} from solid, ammonium iron(II) sulfate hexahydrate, $(NH_4)_2Fe(SO_4)_2 \cdot 6H_2O$. This stock solution will be diluted to one tenth of its concentration to prepare an intermediate standard stock solution. The intermediate stock will be used to prepare standard solutions of Fe^{2+} that will be used to construct a standard curve. The standard curve will be used to determine the concentration of Fe^{2+} in a simulated solution of serum.

Prelab (Show your work for all calculations)

1. How many grams of $CaCO_3$ are needed to prepare 100 mL of a 10,000 µg/dL standard solution of Ca^{2+}?

2. A student begins preparing the Fe^{2+} stock solution by weighing 0.1756 g of $(NH_4)_2Fe(SO_4)_2 \cdot 6H_2O$. The solid is dissolved in a small amount of deionized water then transferred to a 250 mL volumetric flask. The solution is brought to a volume of 250.0 mL with deionized water and mixed. The molar mass of $(NH_4)_2Fe(SO_4)_2 \cdot 6H_2O$ is 392.15 g/mol.

    a. Calculate the molarity of $(NH_4)_2Fe(SO_4)_2 \cdot 6H_2O$ in this stock solution.

    b. Calculate the molarity of Fe^{2+} in this stock solution.

    c. Calculate the concentration of Fe^{2+} in the stock solution in units of g/L.

    d. Calculate the concentration of Fe^{2+} in the stock solution in units of µg/dL.

3. Using the concentration of Fe^{2+} in the stock solution determined in 2d, calculate the concentration of the solution (in µg/dL) that results from taking 10 mL of the stock solution and diluting it to 100 mL. This is the concentration of the Intermediate Stock Solution.

    (HINT: You can use the dilution formula $C_1V_1 = C_2V_2$. The concentrations, C_1 and C_2, can be in any concentration units you like just as long as they are the same for each. They don't have to be moles per liter. Likewise, the volumes, V_1 and V_2, can be in any volume units you like as long as they are the same for each.)

4. Using the concentration of the Intermediate Stock Solution determined in 3, calculate the concentration of Fe^{2+} (in µg/dL) in Standards 1–4 listed in Table 2.1.

5. Read "How to Be Successful in CHM 12901: A Guide to Using Laboratory Equipment and Instrumentation."

6. In a lab to determine the concentration of red dye #40 in Grape Kool-Aid a student made the following calibration curve. The trendline is on the plot.

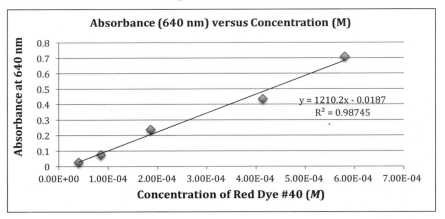

The absorbance of the Kool-Aid solution was 0.41. What was the concentration of red dye #40 in the solution?

7. A student made the following calibration curve in a lab to determine the concentration of iron in garbanzo beans. The trendline is on the graph.

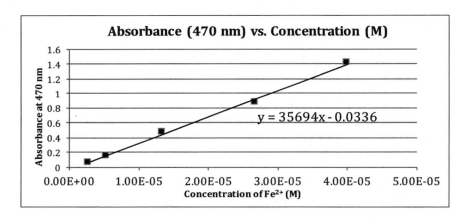

The absorbance of a garbanzo bean solution that had been diluted by a factor of three was 0.528. What was the concentration of the iron in the **original** solution (before dilution)?

Procedure (This procedure is performed by groups of four students)

You and your group will need the following to complete the assay:

Reagents

- 2% hydroxylamine hydrochloride
- Ammonium iron(II) sulfate hexahydrate, $(NH_4)_2Fe(SO_4)_2 \cdot 6H_2O$
- 0.070g/dL FerroZine™
- Concentrated hydrochloric acid (HCl), 12.1M
- "Serum" sample A, B, or C

Equipment

- Parafilm
- USB–USB-B connector
- Power adapter
- LabQuest 2
- Spatula
- SpectroVis spectrometer

Glassware

- 6–disposable cuvettes
- 200-µL and 1000-µL pipettors
- 100-mL beaker, for collecting discarded pipet tips
- Wash bottle of deionized water
- 250-mL volumetric flask
- Medicine dropper
- 100-mL volumetric flask
- 100-mL beaker for collecting waste
- 10-mL pipet
- 100-mL beaker, clean and dry

> The 2% hydroxylamine hydrochloride, deionized water, "serum" samples, and 0.070 µg/dL FerroZine solution are provided in small bottles. There are enough bottles for each group to take one bottle of each solution to their work area. It is important that you read and follow the directions in this procedure so that you and your group can prepare your samples quickly and efficiently.

 WASTE DISPOSAL: FerroZine™ cannot be discarded down the drain. Use a 100-mL beaker to collect all samples for proper disposal. Pour contents of cuvettes into the beaker and rinse them with your wash bottle to remove any remaining waste. When you have completed the experiment, empty the beaker into the waste container in the main hood.

NOTES

NOTES

! CAUTION: The FerroZine™ reagent is very sensitive to iron. You must use clean glassware to prepare solutions. Do not use tap water for any dilutions. The FerroZine™ solution may pick up iron and become slightly purple. This is not unusual. It will not affect your results because the FerroZine™ solution is used to prepare the blank. The blank is then used to zero the spectrometer.

Preparation of a Standard Stock Solution of Fe^{2+}

Tare a clean, dry 100-mL beaker on an analytical balance. The analytical balances are in the small room between each laboratory. Weigh approximately 0.18 g of ammonium iron(II) sulfate hexahydrate in the beaker and record the exact mass of the solid to 4 decimal places.

Add about 30 mL of deionized water to the beaker and swirl to dissolve the solid.

Take the beaker to the hood where the bottle of concentrated hydrochloric acid, 12 M HCl, is stored. Cautiously, add 40 drops of concentrated HCl to the solution. Swirl the solution to mix.

! You must clean up any drops of HCl that are inadvertently spilled in the hood!! Immediately!! Use wet paper towels to remove any spills.

Carefully, pour the iron solution into a 250-mL volumetric flask. Use a wash bottle to rinse the interior of the beaker with deionized water and transfer the wash into the volumetric flask. Repeat the rinsing process again.

Fill the volumetric flask about half full with deionized water. Swirl the contents to mix. Bring the liquid level almost to the mark with deionized water, then use a medicine dropper to bring the volume to the calibration mark. Tightly cover the opening of the flask with a piece of Parafilm and invert the flask several times to mix. What is the concentration of Fe^{2+} in this solution? *Use the exact mass of the $(NH_4)_2Fe(SO_4)_2 \cdot 6H_2O$ to calculate the concentration.* Record the concentration in your notebook.

Preparation of the Standard Intermediate Stock Solution of Fe^{2+}

Rinse a 10-mL pipet with the standard stock solution of Fe^{2+}. Transfer 10.00 mL of the stock solution to a clean 100-mL volumetric flask. Fill the flask to the mark with deionized water. Cover the flask tightly with Parafilm and invert it several times to mix. What is the concentration of this intermediate stock solution? Record the concentration in your notebook.

Preparation of Standard Fe^{2+} Solutions for Standard Curve

You will prepare the blank, standards, and a "serum" sample directly in disposable cuvettes by adding the designated volume of each reagent into each cuvette. Table 2.1 shows the amount of each reagent to add to the cuvettes for each standard. Your instructor will assign your group a "serum" sample either A, B, or C.

Table 2.1. Preparation of Fe^{2+} Standard Solutions.

Standard	Volume of Intermediate Stock Solution of Fe^{2+} (µL)	Volume of 2% Hydroxylamine Hydrochloride (µL)	Volume of Deionized Water (µL)	Volume of 0.070 g/dL FerroZine™ Reagent (µL)	Concentration of Fe^{2+} (µg/dL)
Blank	0	500	1000	500	
1	50	500	950	500	
2	100	500	900	500	
3	200	500	800	500	
4	300	500	700	500	

Obtain five disposable cuvettes. Label the cuvettes B (blank) and 1–4 (standards). Add the reagents to each cuvette in the order that they are listed in the table, i.e., begin with the intermediate stock solution of Fe^{2+}.

1. Attach a tip to the pipettor and add the prescribed amount of intermediate stock solution to each cuvette. There is no need to attach a new tip for each volume of Fe^{2+} solution. Discard the tip.

2. Attach a new tip to the pipettor and add 500 µL of 2% hydroxylamine hydrochloride to each cuvette. Discard the tip.

3. Continue the sample dispensing technique adding the prescribed amount of deionized water to each cuvette. Discard the tip.

4. The last reagent you will add is the FerroZine™ solution. Attach a new tip to the pipetter. With the addition of 500 µL of the 0.070 g/dL FerroZine™ solution, you will mix the sample by repeatedly and slowly pulling the solution in the cuvette into the tip and then slowly dispensing it back into the cuvette. Discard the tip. Use a new tip for each sample.

Prepare "Serum" Sample

1. Label another cuvette "S."

2. Attach a new tip to your pipettor and add 1000 µL of your assigned serum sample to the cuvette. Discard the tip.

3. Attach a new tip and add 500 µL of 2% hydroxylamine. Discard the tip.

4. Attach a new tip and add 500 µL of the FerroZine™ solution. Mix the solution as you did for the standards. Discard the tip.

Connect the SpectroVis Plus to the LabQuest 2
! THE FOLLOWING STEPS MUST BE PERFORMED IN ORDER.

1. Plug in the LabQuest with the power adapter. Turn on the LabQuest and wait for the Meter screen to appear.

2.   Connect the USB-A cable to the LabQuest.

3.   Connect the USB-B end of the cable to the SpectroVis spectrometer.

4.   The LabQuest screen will display **USB: Abs**.

USB-A connect
to LabQuest

USB-B connect
to SpectroVis

Set the Vernier SpectroVis Plus to Zero Absorbance

1.   From the **Sensors** menu, choose **Calibrate** > **USB: Spectrometer**. The calibration dialog box will display the message: "Taking dark sample" then "Waiting 90 seconds for lamp to warm up."

2.   When warmup is complete, wipe the outside of the blank with a Kimwipe and insert it into the spectrophotometer.

3.   Click **Finish Calibration**, then **OK**.

4.   Save the blank in case you need to recalibrate the spectrometer.

Set the Wavelength of the Spectrophotometer to 560 nm

1.   Wipe the outside of the cuvette that contains Standard #1 with a Kimwipe and insert it into the spectrometer.

2.   Tap on the **green arrow** to start data collection. You will see a graph of the spectrum for the $Fe(FerroZine)_3^{4-}$ complex.

3.   Tap on the **red square** to stop data collection.

4.   Move the cursor along the graph to choose the maximum absorbance for the complex. The wavelength and absorbance will be displayed to the right of the graph. The maximum should be near 560 nm. Record the concentration and absorbance of Standard #1 in your notebook.

5.   Now set the collection mode, by tapping the meter icon, .

6.   Tap on the grey **Mode** box. Tap on **Mode** and choose **Time Based.**

7.   Click **OK** and **Discard** the spectrum data.

Absorbance Measurements of the Standard Fe²⁺ Solutions

Now that the parameters are set for the LabQuest and spectrometer, all you need to do to measure the absorbance of a sample is to insert the sample into the spectrometer.

You should have recorded the absorbance of Standard #1 and can now continue with the remaining standards from the least concentrated (#2) to the most concentrated (#4):

1. Wipe the outside of the cuvette that contains Standard #2 with a Kimwipe.

2. Insert the cuvette into the spectrophotometer.

3. Wait a few seconds and record the absorbance displayed and concentration of the standard in your lab notebook.

4. Repeat steps 1–3 to find the absorbance of Standards #3 and #4.

Analysis of the "Serum" Solution

1. Wipe the outside of cuvette **S** with a Kimwipe and insert it into the spectrophotometer.

2. Wait 10 seconds, and record the absorbance value displayed in your notebook.

Transfer the Standard Curve Data to an Excel File

Open Excel. Label column A: Fe²⁺ concentration (µg/dL); and column B: Absorbance. Enter your data from the measurement of the Fe²⁺ standard solutions into the appropriate columns. Save the data.

Cleanup and Waste Disposal

Dispose of solutions containing FerroZine in the waste jar in the main hood.

The disposable cuvettes and pipet tips are discarded in the trash.

Wash all glassware with hot water and soap. Rinse well with tap and deionized water.

Shut down the LabQuest by touching the **Home** icon. Tap **System** > **Shut Down**. Return the LabQuest, adapter, USB connector, and the spectrometer to the box on your lab bench.

Return the volumetric flasks to the drawers in the back of the lab.

Return the bottles of 2% hydroxylamine hydrochloride, deionized water, 0.070 g/dL FerroZine, and "serum" to the reagent bench.

Keep your splash goggles on (over your eyes) until you are ready to leave the lab. Do not take them off or put them on your forehead and stand around talking to your group members. If you have your goggles off, then wait in the hallway to meet your group members after they, too, leave the lab.

NOTES

Data Analysis

Prepare a Standard Curve for the Fe^{2+} Standard Solutions

Prepare a graph of Absorbance versus Concentration of Fe^{2+}. Include a trendline and R^2 value on the graph. Make sure that the graph has a title and the axes are labeled. Print your standard curve for inclusion with your report

Postlab Questions (To be included in lab report)

1. Use your standard curve (trendline) to calculate the concentration of Fe^{2+} in your "serum" sample. You must take into consideration that you diluted the sample when you added 2% hydroxylamine and 0.070 μg/dL FerroZine. Show all steps of your work.

2. Consider the normal serum iron levels given earlier in this document. Based on your experimental results, is the iron level in your serum sample too low or too high for each category? Explain your answer. Simply answering *too low* will not suffice.

CHAPTER 3

Biologically Important Molecules: Amino Acids, Proteins, and Carbohydrates

Introduction

Proteins

Proteins are essential biomolecules in all living organisms. Proteins are comprised of one or more chains of amino acids that are linked in a specific manner. The amino acids have the following general structure:

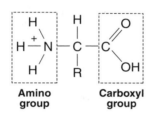

Figure 3.1. General structure of amino acids shown in the fully protonated state. The R represents a distinct side chain for each amino acid.

The amino acids covalently link together forming proteins in a condensation reaction between the α-carboxyl group of one molecule with the amino group of another molecule. (See the condensation reaction in your text.)

There are twenty common amino acids that make up mammalian proteins. The amino acids are separated into two major groups based on whether the side chains are **hydrophilic** or **hydrophobic**. The hydrophilic amino acids are further divided into polar uncharged and polar charged molecules.

At physiological pH, the amino and carboxyl group are also charged. Amino acids do not exist as uncharged molecules because at physiological pH (7.2–7.4) the molecule contains both carboxylic acid and a basic amino group. At physiological pH, the carboxylic acid exists as COO^- and the amino group exists as NH_3^+, a protonated amine. The amino acids are **amphoteric** molecules that behave as either an acid or a base.

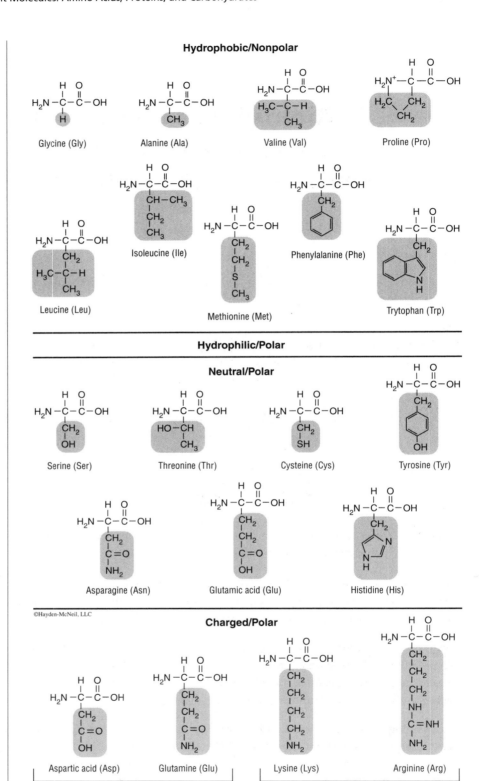

Figure 3.2. Common amino acids.

NOTES

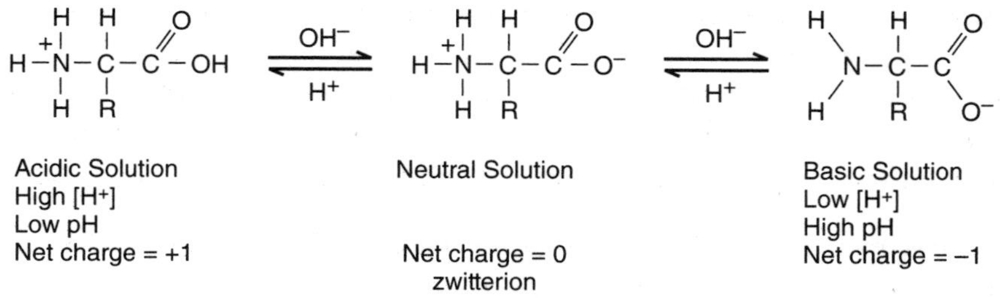

Figure 3.3. Protonation of amino acids at different pHs.

Acidic Solution
High [H+]
Low pH
Net charge = +1

Neutral Solution

Net charge = 0
zwitterion

Basic Solution
Low [H+]
High pH
Net charge = −1

The hydrophobic or hydrophilic characteristics, as well as the charge of the amino acids, contribute to the structure and function of the proteins they form. The chemistry of the amino acids defines the **primary, secondary, tertiary**, and **quaternary** structure of the proteins.

Primary structure

©Hayden-McNeil, LLC

*Typically, proteins contain
100 to 500 amino acids*

Figure 3.4. Primary protein structure.

The **primary** structure of a protein refers to the linear number and order of the amino acid polymer. The polypeptide is held together by **covalent** amide (peptide) bonds. These peptide bonds increase the stability of the molecule because of **resonance** around the bond delocalizing the bonding electrons over more than one chemical bond in the amino acid. See Figure 3.5. The resonance imparts rigidity in this bond and limits free rotation about the bond. This greatly restricts the possible conformations of the polypeptide chain and consequently the behavior of folded proteins.

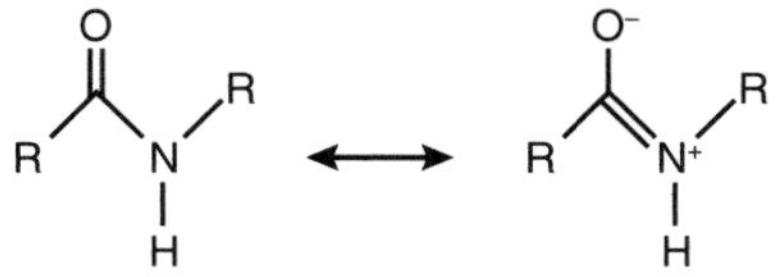

Figure 3.5. Resonance structure of peptide bond imparts stability.

Amino acids contain either hydrophilic or hydrophobic side chains. See Figure 3.2. The interactions between these side chains and the aqueous environment play a major role in the shape of the protein. The folded state of the protein is driven by the balance between the hydrogen bonding of the hydrophilic side

NOTES

chains with the aqueous environment and the repulsive forces between this aqueous environment and the hydrophobic amino acids. Hydrophobic amino acids tend to be repulsed by the aqueous environment and reside within the interior of the protein. This is reflected by the spontaneous folding of the protein, where hydrophobic side chains are folded into the interior of the protein.

The **electrostatic** attraction and repulsion between charged amino acids and the dipole of water are another substantial force in protein folding.

In this laboratory, you will first study the individual amino acids that make up proteins using a qualitative technique known as paper chromatography. Then you will measure the quantity of protein in a solution with an often used technique known as the Bradford assay. Both of these techniques rely on the chemistry of the amino acids.

Chromatographic Separation of Amino Acids: The Building Blocks of Proteins

Chromatography is a technique that is used to separate the components of a mixture. There are many types of chromatography, most of which involve two phases, a *stationary* phase and a *mobile* phase. A component or mixture of components are deposited onto the stationary phase, and the mobile phase is allowed to pass over the stationary phase. The components will separate according to how strongly they absorb to the stationary phase versus how readily they dissolve in the mobile phase. In this way, individual components of the mixture that have different affinities for one of the phases can be separated.

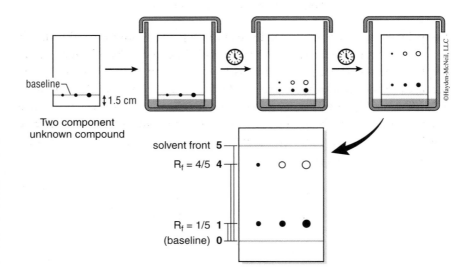

Figure 3.6. A mixture is spotted on the baseline. The TLC plate is placed in a chamber and the solvent moves up the plate. A lid ensures that the atmosphere in the chamber is saturated with solvent. As the solvent moves up the plate the mixture separates into a fast moving spot and a slower moving spot. The retardation factor, R_f, of each spot is found by measuring the distance the spot moved relative to the distance the solvent moved (i.e., for the faster spot the R_f is = 4/5 and for the slower spot the R_f is = 1/5). The R_f of the faster spot is larger, meaning that it has moved farther along the plate (in that solvent) than the slower spot.

In thin layer chromatography (TLC), the stationary phase is a thin layer of absorbent material such as silica gel, alumina, or cellulose. A variety of liquid solvents can be used for the moving (mobile) phase. As the mobile phase passes over the point where the solute has been deposited on the stationary phase, it dissolves the components depending on their solubility. The components that are more soluble in the solvent will be carried the farthest. These components are exchanged back and forth between the two phases. Those components held more strongly by the stationary phase do not move as far as the more soluble components in the moving solvent. The fraction of time a component spends in the mobile phase determines how fast it moves with the solvent. If it spends all of its time in the mobile phase, it will move along with the solvent front. If it spends nearly all of its time in the stationary phase, it will stay near the point of application. By carefully selecting the solvent, sharp separations of dissolved components can be achieved. See Figure 3.6.

In this procedure, you will use paper chromatography to separate and identify amino acids.

You will use a value called the retardation factor or R_f to identify each amino acid. The retardation factor, R_f, of each spot is found by measuring the distance the component moved relative to the distance the solvent moved then using these values to calculate the ratio:

$$\frac{\text{distance traveled by component}}{\text{distance traveled by solvent}} = R_f$$

To visualize the amino acids, your teaching assistant will spray the chromatography paper with a solution containing the compound ninhydrin (2,2-Dihydroxyindane-1,3-dione). The ninhydrin, which is yellow, will react with the free amino group of the amino acid, producing a purple color. The amino acids will appear on the paper as purple spots.

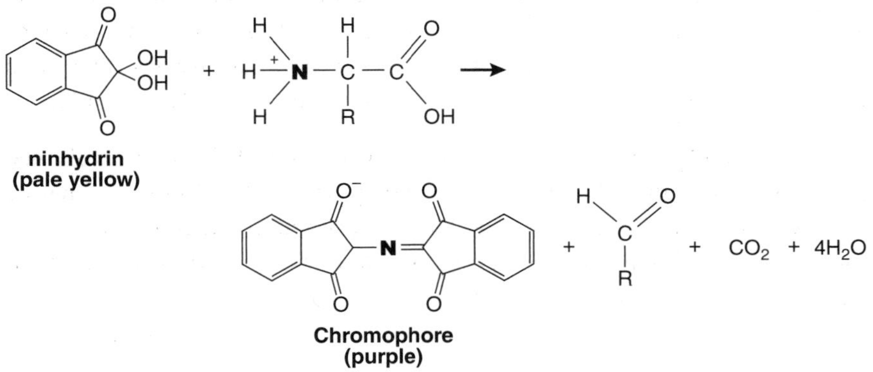

Figure 3.7. Reaction of ninhydrin and an amino acid.

NOTES

The Bradford Protein Assay

The protein concentration of an unknown solution is determined quantitatively by comparing the intensity of color produced in the Bradford assay to the color produced by the bovine serum albumin (BSA) standard solutions containing known concentrations of protein.

The Bradford assay is based on the binding of Coomassie Brilliant Blue G-250 dye to proteins at arginine, tryptophan, tyrosine, histidine, and phenylalanine residues. Under acidic conditions, as the dye binds to a protein, the dye is converted from a red form of the dye to a bluer form. **The intensity of the blue color is directly proportional to the protein concentration**. We can measure the intensity of the color complex using a spectrophotometer. Refer to "How to Be Successful in CHM 12901: A Guide to Using Laboratory Equipment and Instrumentation" at the beginning of this manual for information on the use of a spectrophotometer and the principles of spectroscopy.

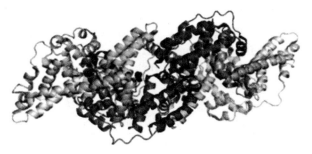

Figure 3.8. Structure of Bovine Serum Albumin PDB ID4F5S. A. Bujacz (2012) Structures of bovine, equine, and leporine serum albumin. Acta Crystallor., Sect. D **68**: 1278–89.

Carbohydrates

Carbohydrates, also known as sugars or saccharides, are another major class of biomolecules found in all cells. Carbohydrates perform many roles in living organisms. Energy is stored in cells as polysaccharides, starches, or glycogen. Carbohydrates can also serve as structural components, such as cellulose which makes up the cell wall in plants. The 5-carbon monosaccharides ribose and deoxyribose are important components in the backbone of DNA and RNA.

Carbohydrates have the general formula $C_nH_{2n}O_n$ or $(CH_2O)_n$, and are divided into monosaccharides, disaccharides, and polysaccharides. A monosaccharide may be further classified by the functional groups within the compound. If the saccharide contains an aldehyde group, it is known as an aldose; if it contains a ketone group, it is known as a ketose.

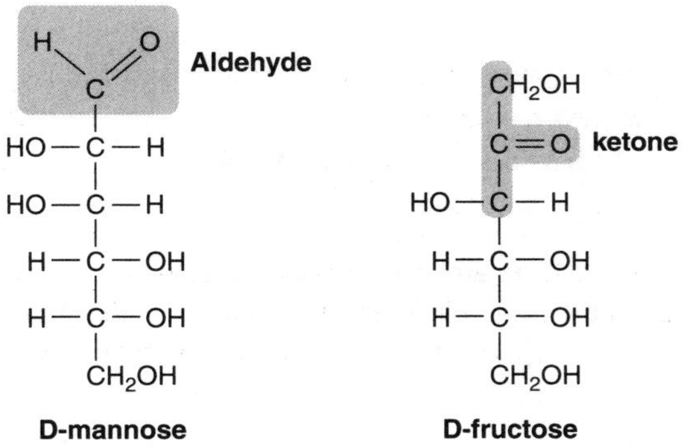

Figure 3.9. D-mannose and D-fructose are examples of aldose and ketose sugars.

The **Tollens' test** (also known as the silver-mirror test) is a qualitative test to distinguish between aldehydes and ketones. In this test, sugars and other molecules with an **aldehyde** group are readily oxidized, whereas ketones are not. The reaction involves the oxidation of aldehydes to the corresponding carboxylic acid using Tollens' reagent. Tollens' reagent is a basic (high pH) alcoholic solution of silver ions coordinated to ammonia, $[Ag(NH_3)_2]^+$. The oxidation of the sugar is accompanied by the reduction of silver ions to metallic silver which forms a mirror on the reaction tube.

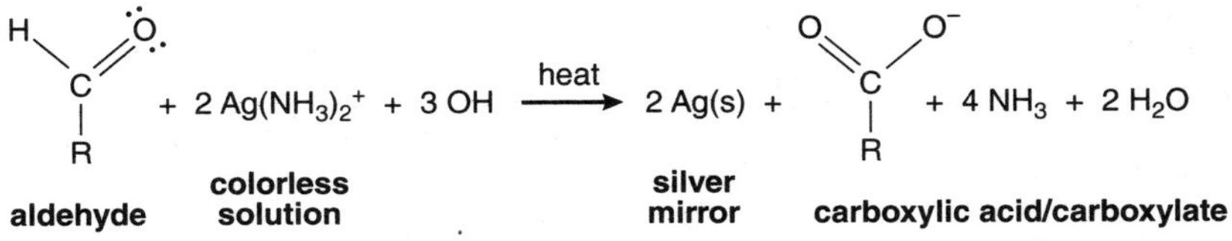

Figure 3.10. Silver mirror test for aldehydes using Tollens' reagent.

Prelab

1. What is an amino acid? What parts of the 20 naturally occurring amino acids are the same? What parts are different? How are they classified?

2. Describe how thin layer chromatography (TLC) works. What is an R_f value, or retardation factor? How will you use TLC in this laboratory?

3. What is the Bradford Assay used for in this laboratory? What information do you get out of it? How does it work?

4. For the Bradford Assay you will generate a standard curve. What is the purpose of a standard curve? How will you use it in this laboratory?

5. What type of chemical reaction occurs during the Tollens' test? Describe why the Tollens' test is sometimes called the silver mirror test.

6. Write out the procedure for this laboratory.

NOTES

Procedure

Some parts of this experiment are performed individually and others as a group of four students; however, each person must record a complete set of observations and data in his/her lab notebook and turn in the duplicate copy on the perforated pages at the end of lab.

 WASTE COLLECTION: There are several waste jars for this experiment. It is very important that the waste produced in this experiment be disposed of in the appropriate containers. Please follow instructions carefully.

WEAR GLOVES: If you leave the lab, take your gloves off and recycle them. Get new gloves when you return to the lab.

Chromatography of Amino Acids (Work Individually)

Materials

For this experiment, you will need the following:

From your teaching assistant

- Sheet of chromatography paper

From your drawer

- Ruler
- 600-mL beaker (clean and dry)

From the shelf near front sink

- Plastic wrap

From the reagent bench or hoods

- Amino acid solutions
    o Aspartic acid
    o Glycine
    o Leucine
    o Tyrosine

- Numbered unknown mixture of amino acids

- Toothpicks

- 2-propanol and 2% ammonia

- Ninhydrin spray

You will also need a pencil. You must use a **pencil** to mark your chromatography paper.

Preparing the Developing Chamber

Label a clean, dry 600-mL beaker as a solvent chamber. Mix 10 mL of 2% aqueous ammonia with 20 mL of 2-propanol in the beaker and cover tightly with plastic wrap.

You must wear gloves while handling the chromatography paper. Your skin continuously sloughs proteins that will react with the ninhydrin spray that we will use to visualize the amino acids. Any place that you touch the paper with your bare fingers will become purple fingerprints and obscure your results.

Applying the Amino Acids to the Stationary Phase (Cellulose)

Obtain a sheet of chromatography paper. Just below the baseline, lightly pencil small hash marks, starting 2.5 cm from the left edge and making marks every 2.0 cm. These marks designate where you will apply the amino acid solutions and the unknown mixture of amino acids. Below each mark, pencil an abbreviation for the amino acid that you intend to apply to the paper. You will apply the unknown mixture of amino acids at intervals across the paper (i.e., along the baseline you would apply asp, unk, gly, unk, leu, unk, etc.). See the list of amino acid solutions on the previous page. Pencil your name at the top of the paper.

Draw a picture of your chromatogram and the application plan in your lab notebook.

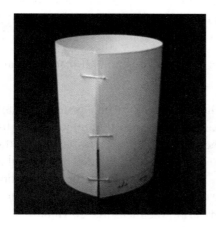

Figure 3.11. Prepare the chromatogram.

To apply the amino acid samples, dip the end of a toothpick into the sample vial. Gently dab the paper with the toothpick to make a small spot (2 mm diameter) of sample on the line above the corresponding name. Do not use a drop hanging from the toothpick. Do not press the toothpick into the paper with so much force that the paper is indented. This will put too much sample on the paper. If you have a hanging drop, first blot the toothpick on a piece of paper towel, then spot your chromatography paper. Using a new toothpick for each solution, continue to spot each amino acid and the unknown mixture onto the paper. Dispose of toothpicks in the trash.

Allow the spots to dry, then carefully roll the sheet into a cylinder and staple the edges 1–2 cm from the top and bottom and again in the middle of the seam, leaving a gap as shown. Do not overlap the edges.

NOTES

Developing the Chromatogram

Place the cylinder into the beaker of solvent. The level of the solvent must be below the baseline. The paper should not touch the sides of the beaker. Cover the jar tightly with plastic wrap. Do not disturb the beakers while the chromatograms are developing. Time needed for development is approximately 60 minutes.

Ideally you should remove your chromatogram from the solvent when the solvent front is 2–3 cm from the top of the paper or at least one hour before the end of the lab period. You will need time to visualize the amino acids and measure the R_f values of the samples. Quickly remove the staples, lay the chromatogram on a piece of paper towel, and mark the solvent front across the entire length of the paper with a pencil. Allow the paper to dry within your student bench hood or in one of the main hoods.

Visualizing the Amino Acids

In the designated main hood, lay the chromatogram flat in the box provided and cautiously spray a fine mist of ninhydrin on the surface of the paper. **YOUR TA WILL DO THIS FOR YOU!** After the paper dries, put the paper in a 100°C oven for 5 to 10 minutes.

The amino acids will react with the ninhydrin and appear as colored spots on the paper.

Circle the spots on the paper lightly with a pencil and mark the center of each amino acid spot. Measure the distance the amino acid has traveled up the paper from the baseline and the distance from the baseline to the solvent front. The distance that the amino acid traveled divided by the total distance traveled by the solvent from the baseline is known as the retardation factor, or R_f, value (see Figure 3.6). The components of the unknown mixture of amino acids can be identified by comparing the measured R_f value with those of the known amino acids.

Sketch the appearance of the chromatogram in your laboratory notebook.

Quantitative Determination of Protein: The Bradford Protein Assay

Materials (Work in groups of four students)

From your teaching assistant

- 1–vial of Bovine Serum Albumin (BSA) stock solution, 20 µg/mL

- 2–vials of BSA of unknown concentration

- 1–vial of Bradford reagent

- 7–disposable cuvettes

From the shelf near front sink

- Parafilm

From the reagent bench or hoods

• Disposable test tubes

From the balance room

• Pipetters and tips

Preparation of Standard Protein Samples

First, you must prepare standard solutions of BSA to construct a standard curve for the protein. Label four disposable test tubes 1–4. In these test tubes, you will prepare 2 mL (2000 µL) of each BSA standard by serial dilution (Figure 3.12). For the serial dilution, you will begin with tube 4, the most concentrated solution. Tube 4 will contain a 1:1 dilution of the stock BSA (20 µg/mL) or a concentration of 10 µg/mL. Thereafter, a 1:1 serial dilution produces the required volume and concentration for each test tube.

Prepare these dilutions by adding 1000 µL of deionized water to each tube with a pipetter. You can use the same pipet tip for dispensing the water into all four tubes. Next, beginning with test tube 4, add 1000 µL of 20 µg/mL BSA stock solution using the pipetter provided and mix. Discard the pipet tip. With a new pipet tip, continue the series of dilutions by transferring 1000 µL of the solution from test tube 4 to tube 3. Mix tube 3 by covering the tube with Parafilm and inverting the tube several times. Repeat the same procedure for the remaining dilutions. Use a new pipet tip for each transfer.

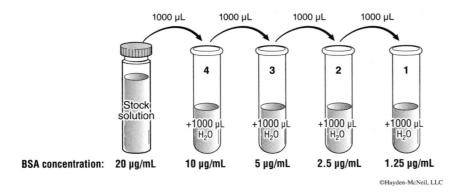

©Hayden-McNeil, LLC

Figure 3.12. Preparation of BSA standard solutions.

Bradford Protein Assay

Unknown protein solutions will be provided by your instructor. Your group will receive two coded vials of protein solution of unknown concentration. Record the code number for each of your tubes in your laboratory notebook.

Label five disposable cuvettes 0–4 and two more disposable cuvettes with the code for your unknown protein samples. Cuvette 0 will contain the blank or control; add 800 µL of deionized water to this cuvette. With the pipetter transfer

NOTES

800 μL of each standard protein to the corresponding cuvette, then transfer 800 μL of each unknown protein to your labeled cuvettes. See Figure 3.13 for guidance.

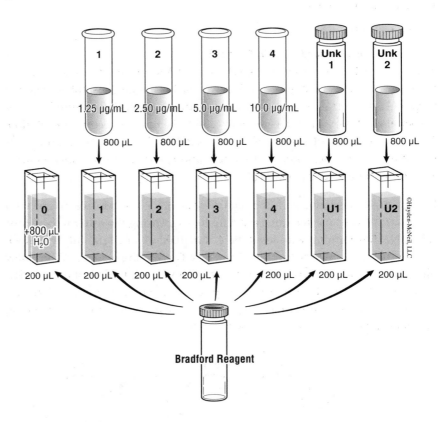

Figure 3.13. Preparing final standard solutions and unknowns for measurement of protein concentration.

Add 200 μL of Bradford dye reagent to all of the cuvettes. Mix the sample by slowly and carefully pulling the solution into the pipet tip then dispensing the solution back into the cuvette. Repeat at least three times. Allow 5 minutes for the color to develop.

Connect the Spectrophotometer to the LabQuest 2
The following steps must be performed in order.

1. Insert the USB-A into the LabQuest.

2. Attach the power adapter to the LabQuest.

3. Turn on the LabQuest and wait for the **Meter** screen to appear.

4. Connect the USB-B end of the cable to the SpectroVis.

5. The LabQuest screen will display **USB: Abs**.

USB-A
connect to
LabQuest

USB-B
connect to
SpectroVis

Set the Vernier SpectroVis Plus to Zero Absorbance

1. Drop the wood block into the spectrometer.

2. From the **Sensors** menu, choose **Calibrate > USB: Spectrometer**. The calibration dialog box will display the message: "Waiting 90 seconds for lamp to warm up."

3. When warmup is complete, wipe the outside of cuvette 0 with a Kimwipe and insert it into the spectrophotometer.

4. Click **Finish Calibration** then **OK**.

5. Save the blank in case you need to recalibrate the spectrometer.

Set the Wavelength of the Spectrophotometer to 595 nm

1. Wipe the outside of the **cuvette 4 (standard solution 4)** with a Kimwipe and insert it into the spectrometer.

2. Tap on the **green arrow** to start data collection. You will see a graph of the spectrum for the protein-Coomassie Brilliant Blue complex.

3. Tap on the **red square** to stop data collection.

4. Move the cursor along the graph to choose the maximum absorbance. The wavelength and absorbance will be displayed to the right of the graph. The maximum should be near 595 nm. Record the maximum wavelength, concentration, and absorbance of solution 4 in your notebook.

5. Now set the collection mode by tapping the meter icon, ⊘.

6. Tap on the grey **Mode** box. Tap on **Mode** and choose **Time Based**.

7. Click **OK** and **Discard** the spectrum data.

Measurement of the Standard Protein Solutions

Now that the parameters are set for the LabQuest and spectrometer, all you need to do to measure absorbance of a sample is to insert the sample into the spectrometer.

NOTES

You should have recorded the absorbance of standard solution 4 and can now continue with the remaining standard solutions from the least concentrated (1) to the most concentrated (5) and your unknown protein samples:

1. Wipe the outside of standard 1 with a Kimwipe and insert it into the spectrophotometer.

2. Wait a few seconds and record the absorbance displayed and concentration of the solution in your lab notebook.

3. Repeat with the other standard solutions.

Measurement of the Unknown Protein Solutions

1. Wipe the outside of unknown 1 with a Kimwipe and insert it into the spectrometer.

2. Wait a few seconds and record the absorbance displayed in your lab notebook.

3. Repeat with the unknown 2.

Transfer the Data to an Excel File

Open Excel. Enter your data from the measurement of the standard protein solutions macro scale solutions into the appropriate columns.

Save the data.

All solutions MUST be measured within 15 minutes after the addition of Bradford dye because the color complex will begin to fade with time.

Pour all solutions down the drain with plenty of water. Disposable cuvettes can be discarded in the trash can. Disposable test tubes and vials must be discarded in the glass trash (blue and white box). Shut down the LabQuest by tapping the Home icon, then tap System > Shut Down. Disconnect the LabQuest and spectrometer and return the LabQuest, spectrophotometer, USB connecter, and DC adapter to the box on your lab bench.

Silver Mirror or Tollens' Test (Work Individually)

Materials

From the shelf near front sink

• Parafilm

From the reagent bench or hoods

• Disposable test tubes

• 6 M nitric acid

• Methanol

- Test solutions, 5%
  - Deionized water, blank
  - A ketone
  - An aldehyde
  - Glucose
- 8% silver nitrate
- 12% ammonium nitrate
- 10% sodium hydroxide
- Waste jar for methanol
- Waste jar for Tollens' test

From your drawer

- Wash bottle

For this test, you may perform the procedure individually. You will be testing a blank (deionized water), a ketone, an aldehyde, and glucose.

Obtain four disposable test tubes from the reagent bench. The test tubes must be carefully prepared before performing the Tollens' test. Rinse the test tubes with the following solutions in the order indicated:

1. Deionized water

2. 20 drops of 6 M nitric acid (discard nitric acid in the Tollens' waste jar)

3. Deionized water

4. 20 drops of methanol (discard in the "Waste Jar for Methanol")

5. Deionized water

Label the four tubes with the solutions that you will test in the following manner: 0 = blank (deionized water), 1 = ketone, 2 = aldehyde, and 3 = glucose. Add 8 drops of the test solutions to the appropriate tube. As you add the drops of solution, roll the tube to wet the walls of the tube.

For the test, add reagents to each tube in the following order:

1. 4 drops 8% silver nitrate solution

2. 4 drops 12% ammonium nitrate solution

3. 8 drops 10% sodium hydroxide solution

Quickly cover the tubes with Parafilm. While holding your fingers over the covered tubes, shake vigorously. The mirror should form within one minute. Continue shaking the tubes for 3 minutes. After 5 minutes, record your observations.

NOTES

Dispose of the solutions in the "Waste Jar for Tollens' Test." It is critical that solutions from this test be disposed of in the appropriate waste jar. It is also important that no other solutions be put into this waste jar. There is the possibility of silver azide formation, a highly explosive compound.

If you would like to keep your mirrored test tubes, rinse the tubes gently with deionized water several times and allow the tubes to air dry. Otherwise, dispose of tubes in the glass trash.

Cleanup and Waste Disposal

Dispose of waste in appropriate waste containers found in the main hood.

All solutions from BSA analysis must be discarded. Dispose of vials in the glass trash. Cuvettes are discarded in the trash. Clean your work area.

©Hayden-McNeil, LLC

Keep your splash goggles on over your eyes as you complete the lab report. Do not take off your splash goggles until you are ready to leave lab. Do not take them off or put them on your forehead and stand around talking to your group members. If you have your goggles off, then wait in the hallway to meet your group members or others after they leave the lab.

Lab Notebook Pages

Before you leave lab, turn in the duplicate pages from your lab notebook where you recorded data and observations as you completed the lab work.

The Laboratory Report

Your group is to prepare one lab report following the guidelines described on pages x–xii.

Remember, it is your responsibility as a group to ensure that everyone whose name is on the report participated as fully as possible in the project.

The due date and time will be communicated to you by your instructor. Reports will usually be due at the beginning of lab the week after the experiment was completed.

Postlab Questions (To be included in lab report)

1.   Which amino acids have the highest and lowest R_f values?

2.   Construct a table that lists the R_f data from each amino acid. It is important that the data are well recognizable and clearly understandable.

3.   Which amino acids compose your unknown? Explain or justify your answer based on experimental evidence.

4.   Construct a graph of your Bradford protein assay data. On the y-axis, plot absorbance values, and on the x-axis, plot concentration of BSA. **Remember to use appropriate units and to title your graph.** Using your graph, determine the protein concentration of the two unknown solutions.

5.   Based on your results of the Tollens' test, is glucose an aldehyde or ketone?

NOTES

CHAPTER 4

Biologically Important Molecules: Lipids and Nucleic Acids

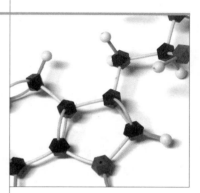

Introduction

Lipids

Lipids are a group of biomolecules that are classified by a physical property instead of their chemical structure or a particular functional group. Lipids are all biomolecules that are insoluble in water. Lipids have a very high proportion of nonpolar C–H bonds that are soluble in nonpolar solvents.

The main groups of lipid biomolecules are triglycerols (fats and oils), phospholipids (cell membrane bilayer), prostaglandins (chemical messengers), steroids (hormones), and terpenes (pigments and some vitamins).

In this experiment, you will extract the fat from potato chips. The lipids extracted are all triglycerols more commonly known as triglycerides. A triglyceride is formed in a dehydration reaction of glycerol with three fatty acids.

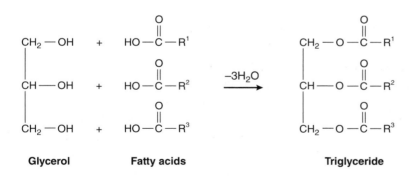

Glycerol   **Fatty acids**   **Triglyceride**

Figure 4.1. Formation of triglyceride from glycerol and three fatty acids.

The R^n represents various fatty acids. Fatty acids are long chain hydrocarbons with a carboxyl group at its end. Fatty acids have an even number of carbons in the chain. The most common fatty acids contain between 12 and 20 carbons. Fatty acids without double bonds are called **saturated fatty acids**. Fatty acids

NOTES

with double bonds are known as **unsaturated fatty acids**. Figure 4.2 shows examples of both a saturated and unsaturated fatty acid. Note that the unsaturated acid is a *trans-fat*, meaning the double bond is in the trans isomer.

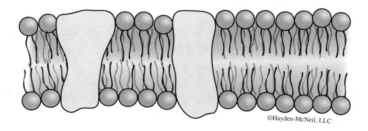

Figure 4.2. Saturated and unsaturated fatty acids.

In this experiment, you will also encounter the chemistry of another class of lipids: the phospholipids. The phospholipids make up the cell membranes in the form of a lipid bilayer. Phospholipids compose the cell membrane and consist of a polar phosphate/diglyceride head and two fatty acid tails.

For the isolation of DNA, the cell membrane must be disrupted to release the DNA and cell contents. We will use detergent to solubilize the cell membrane. Detergents are partially hydrophobic and partially hydrophilic. The detergent moves into the cell membrane, disrupting the bilayer and releasing the cell's contents.

©Hayden-McNeil, LLC

Figure 4.3. Intact region of a lipid bilayer membrane with two proteins.

Analysis of Fat Content in Potato Chips

The general consensus is that no more than 30% of Calories should come from fat. However, 30% of Calories does not necessarily correspond to the *amount* of fat in your food. Different types of food have different energy values. For example, one gram of a protein or carbohydrate has an energy value of 4 kcal/g (Cal/g), while one gram of fat has an energy value of 9 kcal/g (Cal/g). Note that a Calorie as it appears on a nutrition label is the equivalent of 1000 calories, where one calorie is the energy required to raise 1 g by 1 degree Celsius.

Let's take a look at the Big Mac® nutrition label [530 Cal (211 g)]:

	Weight (g)	% By Weight	Calories	% By Calories
Fat	27 g	13%	27 g × 9 Cal/g = 243 Cal	46%
Carbohydrates	47 g	22%	47 g × 4 Cal/g = 188 Cal	35%
Protein	24 g	11%	24 g × 4 Cal/g = 96 Cal	18%

Only about 13% of the weight is from fat, but 46% of the Calories are from fat! Obviously, determining the content of fat in foods is very important.

Potatoes contain a very small amount of fat—just 0.1%—but they will absorb some of the cooking oil when fried. In this experiment you will determine the percent of fat, by weight, in three different kinds of Ruffles® brand potato chips: original, reduced fat, and baked. You will determine the fat absorbed by the chips by mixing the chips with a relatively nonpolar solvent that will dissolve the fat and not dissolve the water-soluble components of the food such as proteins and carbohydrates. You will then pour the solvent off of the chips, collecting the fat and solvent together. This is known as a solvent extraction. The solvent is then evaporated from the fat and the weight of the fat is measured. Our procedure is rather simplistic. The analysis used to determine fat in food for nutrition labels is more complete than just a simple solvent extraction. You will compare your results to the label information by calculating the percent error in your measurements using the following equation:

$$\text{Percent error} = \frac{|\text{Actual} - \text{Theoretical}|}{\text{Theoretical}} \times 100\%$$

where the "Actual" value is the mass percent of fat that you find experimentally and the "Theoretical" value is calculated from the package information.

Another useful calculation is percent recovery:

$$\text{Percent recovery} = \frac{\text{mass of fat recovered}}{\text{theoretical mass of fat}} \times 100\%$$

Percent recovery allows you to calculate how much of a compound or solution was lost through a process. Like percent error, this is a useful calculation to determine the effectiveness of a process or technique.

Nucleic Acids

There are two types of nucleic acids: deoxyribonucleic acid (DNA) and ribonucleic acid (RNA). DNA and RNA are made up of polymers of nucleotides. Each **nucleotide** unit is made up of a **nitrogenous base**, a **5-carbon sugar** (pentose), and a **phosphate** group. The function of nucleic acid molecules is to encode, transmit, and express genetic material.

NOTES

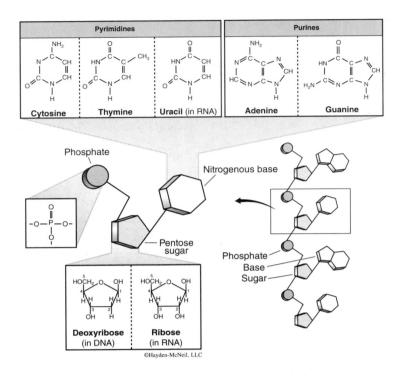

Figure 4.4. Nucleotide components.

The polymers of nucleotides are formed by the dehydration between the hydroxyl group of one nucleotide and the phosphate group of another nucleotide.

Figure 4.5. Formation of nucleotide dimer.

DNA molecules do not exist as a single polymer of nucleotides, but as two paired polymers that fold around each other to form a double helix. The two polymers run in opposite directions. The phosphate groups form the outer backbone of the helix with the nitrogenous bases in the center of the helix. The helix is stabilized by the hydrogen-bonding and hydrophobic nature of the bases.

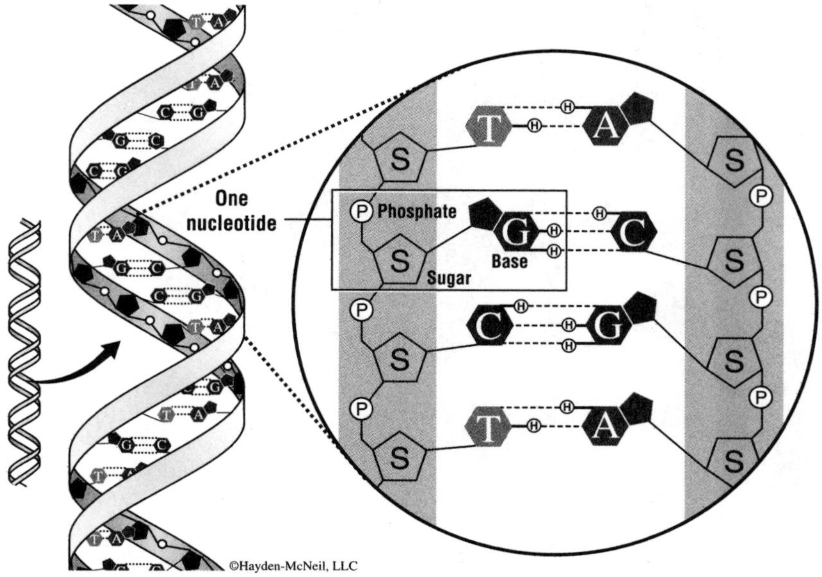

©Hayden-McNeil, LLC

Figure 4.6. Double helix structure of DNA is stabilized by the hydrogen bonding of the nitrogenous bases.

RNA is quite similar to DNA except for a few chemical differences. The RNA molecule contains a hydroxyl group at the number 2 carbon and an RNA polymer is made up of a different complement of nitrogenous bases. The RNA molecule also exists as a single polymer strand, so it does not have the helical shape that a DNA molecule exhibits.

DNA molecules are very large. The human genome contains over a million bases. If the DNA strands were laid out end to end, their length would be as much as 3 meters in length. The X-shaped structure of the chromosome that we often see representing the human genome is achieved by supercoiling of the DNA molecule. In this structure, the DNA is coiled around clusters of proteins known as histone proteins. This DNA-protein complex is known as a nucleosome and is further condensed to form a supercoiled fiber of DNA that forms a chromosome.

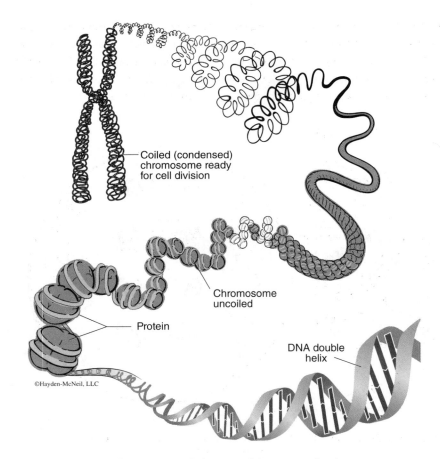

Coiled (condensed)
chromosome ready
for cell division

Chromosome
uncoiled

Protein

DNA double
helix

©Hayden-McNeil, LLC

Figure 4.7. Coiled nature of the DNA molecule.

Isolating DNA from Strawberries

The DNA is found within the nucleus. The supercoiled DNA is protected from the cell environment by a nuclear envelope made up of two lipid bilayers: an inner membrane and outer membrane. RNA is found mostly in the cytoplasm of the cell. DNA and RNA are also found within other organelles such as the mitochondria.

The entire cell is protected or contained within a cell membrane, which is another lipid bilayer. In plants, such as a strawberry, the entire cell is also enveloped by a rigid cell wall made up of cellulose fibers.

To isolate or extract the DNA from the strawberry we must break down the cell wall, cell membrane, and nuclear membrane to release the DNA without destroying the DNA polymer. The DNA is also associated with DNA binding proteins that must be denatured (unfolded).

Isolation of DNA involves three basic steps:

1. **Cell Disruption/Homogenization**: To release the DNA from the nuclei of the strawberry cell, the cell walls, cell membranes, and nuclear membranes must first be broken down. This is done by breaking up and mashing the strawberries to disrupt the cell tissues. Adding detergent and sodium ions (we use Dawn dishwashing liquid and sodium chloride) will solubilize lipid membranes and denature proteins.

2. **Deproteinization**: The cell's protein must be precipitated, separating it from the DNA that will remain in solution. There are also DNA-binding proteins that must be stripped from the DNA. Sodium chloride (salt) is added to the homogenizing medium to further denature and precipitate these proteins in the strawberry cell. The protein and cell debris is removed from the homogenate mechanically.

3. **Precipitation of DNA**: When ice-cold 2-propanol is added to the homogenate, all components of the homogenate stay in solution except DNA, which precipitates at the interface of the alcohol and homogenate layers.

Dische Reaction (Optional: ask your TA if you will be required to perform this test.)
The Dische test can be used to qualitatively or quantitatively test for DNA colorimetrically. The test reagent contains sulfuric acid, a strong acid, which hydrolyzes the nucleic acids to sugars, bases, and phosphoric acid. The Dische reagent reacts specifically with deoxyribose sugars to form a blue complex.

Prelab

1. What is DNA made up of? Where is DNA located in the cell?

2. A Snicker's serving size is one bar (57 g), 13.6 g of which are fat. How much fat is in a 10 g sample?

3. You extract 1.96 g of fat from the sample above. What was your percent recovery (NOT % ERROR!)?

4. In your laboratory notebook, record the experimental procedure you will follow in lab (this does not mean to write it word for word from this procedure!). The procedure is your experimental plan and can be organized as an outline, a flowchart, or a numbered list of steps. You should also include a statement of the purpose of the experiment, notes on safety, and a reference. The copy of your procedure on the duplicate pages of your lab notebook is due at the beginning of lab.

NOTES

Procedure

! WARNING: 2-propanol is very flammable. Keep all containers of 2-propanol closed or covered with a watch glass. All work must be completed within a student bench hood. These hoods are located in the cabinets below the main hoods. Set this bench hood within the metal frame around the exhaust grill on the lab bench at your workstation. Check to make sure that air is being drawn through this hood before beginning your work. All steps in the procedure that involve 2-propanol should be performed in the student bench hood.

EATING IS STRICTLY FORBIDDEN IN THE LABORATORY.

Analysis of Fat Content in Potato Chips

From your group's lab drawers:

- 3–250-mL beakers

- 3 spatulas

- 3–100-mL beakers

- 3 watch glasses

- 3 long-stem funnels

- 3 nichrome triangles

Chemicals

- 15 g of each type of potato chip (regular, reduced fat, and baked)

- 225 mL of 2-propanol (in a hood)

Other materials

- Ring stand (on your bench)

- Iron ring (drawer in back of laboratory)

- Filter paper

- Boiling beads (shelf beside front sink)

First, you will need to collect some data from the nutritional label for each of the potato chips. For each type of chip, record the label's "Nutritional Facts" for 1) serving size (mass) and 2) total fat per serving (mass).

Label three clean, dry 250-mL beakers with the types of potato chips that you will analyze: original, reduced fat, and baked. Weigh each 250-mL beaker on a balance and record the mass to two places beyond the decimal, 0.01 g. Add about 15 g of potato chips to each beaker and record the mass of the beaker + chips to two places beyond the decimal.

Gently break up the chips with a metal spatula. Crush the chips until the pieces are about 5 mm.

NOTES

Obtain 225 mL of 2-propanol in a 250-mL beaker. Add 50 mL of 2-propanol to each beaker and stir for 1 minute. Cover each beaker with a watch glass and let them stand for 10 minutes, stirring every 2 minutes.

In the meantime, place two boiling beads into three clean, dry 100-mL beakers (2 beads per beaker). Label the beakers appropriately and weigh each beaker + beads to three places beyond the decimal, 0.001 g. Record the mass of each beaker.

Place a funnel in a ring stand above each 100-mL beaker. See following figure. Make sure that the bottom of the funnel is inside the beaker, but is not so low that it will touch the extract. Fold a piece of filter paper in half, then in half again (it should be in quarters now). Pull apart the filter paper so that one layer of filter paper is on one side and three are on the other. This should make a cone shape. Slide your cone into your glass funnel.

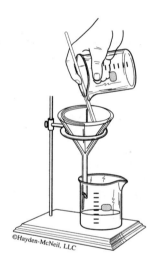

©Hayden-McNeil, LLC

Figure 4.8. Schematic of using a funnel.

Use the technique illustrated above to slowly pour the 2-propanol/fat extract through the filter paper. Place a clean, dry glass stirring rod over the beaker, bisecting the spout. Place your index finger over the rod to hold it in place and pour the extract down the glass stir rod and into the funnel. Pour only the extract, not the chips, into the funnel. Keep the beakers covered with a watch glass until all the extract has been filtered.

As soon as the extract has been poured off, add another 25 mL of 2-propanol to the potato chips in each beaker. Stir. Allow to sit another 10 minutes, stirring every 2 minutes.

Filter the second portion of 2-propanol/fat extract.

Set up one or two hot plates within the student bench hoods. Place white ceramic hot pads beside each hot plate.

NOTES

Place the 100-mL beakers of extract on a hot plate within a student bench hood. Begin heating the extract at a setting of "6" and lower the heat setting to 2 or 3 as the sample begins to boil too vigorously. The sample must boil to remove the 2-propanol but heating too vigorously may cause the solution to spatter out of the beaker. You do not want to lose sample. The fat has a much higher boiling point (about 200°C) than 2-propanol (83°C). CAUTION: Do not leave the beaker unattended. Do not burn the fat!

When all the 2-propanol has been removed from the sample, take the beaker from the hot plate (use several paper towels folded together as a hot pad) and place it on the heat resistant pad. Allow the samples to cool to room temperature.

Find the mass of the beaker + beads + fat to three places beyond the decimal.

Remove the boiling beads from the beaker and transfer them to the collection jar provided. Discard the potato chips and filter paper in the trash as well. Dispose of the fat and any leftover 2-propanol in the Waste Jar for Fat and 2-propanol.

WASH YOUR GLASSWARE IMMEDIATELY WITH HOT, SOAPY WATER.

Isolation of DNA from Strawberries

Your group will be isolating DNA from strawberries using common household chemicals. The DNA molecule is very fragile, so it is important to follow all instructions carefully. You must wear gloves to prevent the nucleases on your skin from contaminating the glassware and destroying the DNA.

Materials
Each group will need a 250-mL beaker of ice to cool the 2-propanol. The ice machine is in the hall beside the storeroom.

From your group's lab drawers

- 2–250-mL beakers
- 50-mL graduated cylinders
- Large stir rod
- 600-mL beaker
- 2–100-mL beakers
- Small stir rod
- Small test tube

From the reagent bench or hoods

- NaCl
- Dawn dishwashing liquid
- 3 strawberries
- 55 mL 2-propanol (put on ice)

Other materials

- Plastic Ziploc bag
- Cheesecloth
- Rubber band
- Ice

Cell Disruption/Homogenization

Prepare the homogenizing media: To a 250-mL beaker, add 1.5 g NaCl(s), 8 mL of colorless Dawn dishwashing liquid, and 45 mL of deionized water. Stir the homogenizing medium until the sodium chloride has dissolved and the solution is well mixed.

Obtain three strawberries and remove the green tops. Put three strawberries into a plastic bag, push all the air out and seal the bag tightly. For 2 minutes, squeeze and mash the strawberries with your fingers.

Add the homogenizing media to the bag. Push all the extra air out of the bag and seal the bag tightly. Squeeze and mash the strawberries with your finger for 1 more minute.

Deproteinization

Prepare to filter the homogenate to remove some of the protein and other plant material. Drape the cheesecloth over a clean 600-mL beaker and secure the cloth with a rubber band. See Figure 4.9 below.

Figure 4.9. Set-up for filtration through cheesecloth.

Pour the homogenate into the middle of the cheesecloth. Allow the homogenate to filter through the cheesecloth for 10 minutes, then gather the sides of the cheesecloth into a bundle **without** squeezing the contents, and discard the cheesecloth and excess strawberry material in the trash.

NOTES

Precipitation of DNA

Pour 30 mL of your filtered homogenate into a clean 100-mL beaker. Pour 50 mL of ice-cold 2-propanol into a 50-mL graduated cylinder. Tilt the beaker of homogenate and very slowly pour the cold propanol down the side of the beaker. The alcohol should form a one-inch deep layer on top of the homogenate. Do not allow the propanol and homogenate to mix. The DNA is insoluble in propanol and will precipitate at the interface of the two liquids.

Add 20 drops of 2 M sulfuric acid to a small test tube. Label the test tube "DNA." Spool or wind the stringy DNA onto a small glass rod by rotating the rod in one direction at the interface of the two solutions in the beaker. Transfer the DNA to the test tube of sulfuric acid and mix gently. You will use this sample for the Dische reaction.

Do not dispose of the homogenate until you have tested your sample for deoxyribose with the Dische reaction. You may need DNA for duplicate tests.

The Dische Reaction: Testing for Deoxyribose in DNA (Optional: ask your TA if you will be required to perform this test.)

From your group's lab drawers

- Small test tubes
- 100-mL beaker
- Stir rod

Chemicals

- 2 M sulfuric acid
- Dische reagent

Other materials

- Hot plate
- Waste jar

Prepare a boiling water bath. Fill a 100-mL beaker with about 50 mL of deionized water. Adjust the heat setting to 6. Label a small test tube "control." Place 20 drops of 2 M sulfuric acid (H_2SO_4) into the test tube.

After the water begins to boil, put the "DNA" and "control" test tubes in the boiling water bath for 15 minutes then turn the heat off. Remove the test tubes using a test tube clamp and allow the test samples to cool for 5 minutes.

Slowly and carefully add 40 drops of Dische reagent to each test tube, then stir to mix. Turn the hot plate back on to a setting of 6. Put the tubes back into the boiling water bath and heat the bath to boiling again. Boil for an additional 5 minutes. Remove the tubes from the water bath and allow to cool.

Strawberry debris may be present in the test solution, lending a red color to the solution. Due to the red debris, a positive Dische test may appear purple. Observe the contents of each test tube and compare to the picture of positive and negative tests for DNA posted in your laboratory. Record your observations and conclusions in your notebook.

Dispose of the contents in the "Waste Jar for Dische Test Solutions."

Leftover homogenate may be poured down the drain with plenty of water. Any unused propanol can be disposed of in the "Waste Jar for Fat and 2-Propanol."

Waste Disposal and Cleanup

Put all waste into the appropriate waste jar. Wash all of your glassware with hot water and dishwashing liquid. Rinse the glassware with hot tap water, then deionized water. Keep your safety goggles on until you have cleaned your work area and are leaving lab. Lock your lab drawer before leaving lab.

Data Analysis

Each lab report should contain a Data Summary similar to the table shown below. As a part of the Data Analysis section of each report include all sample calculations.

	Ruffles® Potato Chips		
	Original	Reduced Fat	Baked
Mass of 250-mL beaker			
Mass of 250-mL beaker with potato chips			
Mass of potato chips			
Mass of 100-mL beaker and boiling beads			
Mass of 100-mL beaker, beads, and extracted fat			
Mass of extracted fat			
Mass percent of fat (experimental)			
Mass of one serving (package)			
Mass of fat per serving (package)			
Mass percent of fat (theoretical)			
Percent error			
Percent recovery			

Lab Notebook Pages

Before you leave lab, turn in the duplicate pages from your lab notebook where you recorded data and observations as you completed the lab work.

NOTES

The Laboratory Report

Your group is to prepare one lab report following the guidelines and outline described on pages x–xii.

Remember, it is your responsibility as a group to ensure that everyone whose name is on the report participated as fully as possible in the project.

The due date and time will be communicated to you by your instructor. Reports will usually be due at the beginning of lab the week after the experiment was completed.

Postlab Questions

1. How does adding 2-propanol to the chips allow you to extract the fat while leaving behind other components of the chips?

2. How many Calories are from fat for each type of potato chip? What is your percent error? Percent recovery?

3. Why is it easier to remove the fat from the original Ruffles?

4. In this experiment, we spooled DNA on a rod. What structural characteristic gives us the ability to spool the DNA?

5. What was the purpose of adding salt to the homogenization solution?

CHAPTER 5

Molecular Geometry and Polarity

5

Objectives

At the end of this activity you should be able to:

- Write Lewis structures for molecules.

- Classify bonds as nonpolar covalent, polar covalent, or ionic based on electronegativity differences.

- Recognize exceptions to the octet rule; draw accurate representations.

- Describe three-dimensional shapes of simple molecules based on VSEPR theory.

- Predict polarity based on geometry and individual dipole moments.

Introduction

The substances in our world exhibit remarkably different properties. At room temperature some substances are solids, others liquids, and others gases. Some participate in sudden chemical reactions, whereas others are quite inert and unreactive. Perhaps most remarkably, this wonderful diversity occurs even though the substances are comprised of a limited number of elements. Indeed, only a very small number of different elements are present in almost any pure substance we encounter in the environment or the laboratory. How can this wide diversity of properties be explained?

A key to understanding the wide range of physical and chemical properties of substances is recognizing that atoms *combine* with other atoms to form molecules or compounds and that the *shape or geometry* of a collection of atoms strongly affects the properties of that substance. One reason this occurs is because the

NOTES

distribution of charge in a molecule affects many properties of the substance. For example, if the negative charge is concentrated in one region of a molecule its properties will be widely different than if the charge is distributed evenly throughout the entire molecule.

In this investigation you will examine a theory that chemists use to explain different aspects of chemical bonding: *Valence-shell electron-pair repulsion* (VSEPR) theory. Attention will be given to how molecules are arranged in different shapes and how chemists can predict the geometry of a given molecule. It will then be shown how a molecule's shape, along with electronegativity differences for its atoms, determine the molecule's polarity. As previously suggested, the best way to understand and predict the physical and chemical properties of substances in our world is by understanding their structure at the molecular level.

Discussion of Activities

In this investigation, you will complete activities that ask you to examine molecular geometry and molecular polarity. These activities are based on computer simulations and ball-and-stick models. **All of these activities can be discussed with classmates and/or completed in small groups, but you each must hand in your own completed packet.**

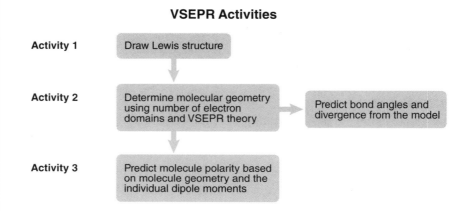

The VSEPR model can be used to predict the geometry of molecules and poly-atomic ions. *Molecular geometry* describes the positions of the atoms in relation to each other. Included in the description are the *bond angles*, the angles made by the lines joining the bonded atoms. In order to predict geometry using the VSEPR model, we need to know the number of electron pairs in the valence shell of the central atom. That can easily be determined by drawing a Lewis structure.

Activity 1: Drawing Lewis Structures

Guidelines for Drawing Lewis Structures

1. Determine the total number of valence electrons; for polyatomic ions remember to adjust for charge.

2. Arrange atoms in a skeleton structure and connect them with single bonds.

    If you are working with a molecule or ion that has three or more atoms, the least electronegative atom is most likely to be the central atom (remembering that hydrogen can only form one bond and therefore is never a likely candidate to be the central atom).

3. Complete octets of the terminal atoms (remember H atoms can only accommodate two electrons).

4. If not all of the valence electrons have been used place any extra electrons on the central atom.

    Extra electrons placed on the central atom may in some cases bring the number to more than eight. This is called *expansion of the valence shell* and is an exception to the octet rule; this is acceptable for atoms in the **third period and below**.

5. If the central atom does not have an octet, use lone pairs from terminal atoms to form multiple bonds.

    Only the second period elements C, N, O, and sometimes S (in combination with C or O) form multiple bonds. This leads to another exception to the octet rule, i.e., when an atom like Be is combined with either hydrogen or halogens, as in BeH_2. Since Be does not form multiple bonds, the central atom is electron deficient.

If more than one acceptable Lewis structure can be drawn by simply choosing a lone pair from a different terminal atom to form a double bond with the central atom, the different structures are called *resonance forms*. The "extra" electron pair is *delocalized*, or spread out among the possible bonding sites.

NOTES

Table 5.1. Drawing Lewis Structures and Determining Electron and Bonding Domains.

	Sketch of Lewis Structure	Does the Structure Violate the "Octet Rule"?	Number of Electron Domains (Central Atom)	Number of Bonding Domains (Central Atom)
H_3O^+				
H_2O				
BF_3				
CO_2				
XeF_6				

One reason Lewis structures are useful is because they help to identify the number of *electron domains*, or regions of high electron density, about a central atom. An electron domain can be a bonding pair, a lone pair, or a double or triple bond. A multiple bond is counted as one domain.

The Lewis structure for HCN is shown below. Notice that the central carbon atom has two electron domains (a single bond and a triple bond) and also two *bonding domains*. The nitrogen atom also has two electron domains (a lone pair of electrons and a triple bond) but only one bonding domain. The hydrogen atom only has one electron domain (the single bond) and one bonding domain.

$$H-C\equiv N\colon$$

Activity 2: VSEPR and Predicting Molecular Geometry

Using Chrome, go to https://phet.colorado.edu/en/simulation/ molecule-shape. Press play. Choose Model.

Once we have the Lewis structure, we have the information needed to predict the geometry. It's important to remember that what we really want to know is the *molecular geometry*—the positions of the atoms in relation to each other. The molecular geometry is dependent on the electron domain geometry; that is why the initial step is drawing the appropriate Lewis structure! As previously noted, the simple concept behind valence-shell electron-pair repulsion theory (VSEPR) is the idea that electron pairs in the valence shell of an atom will repel each other and arrange themselves as far apart as possible. This arrangement of electron pairs determines the geometry of the molecule or polyatomic ion.

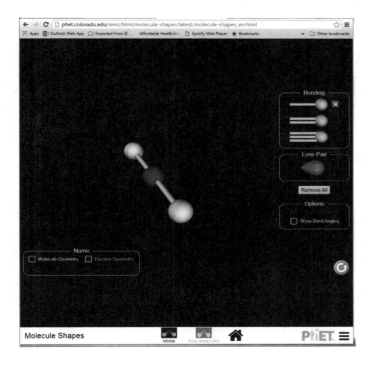

Figure 5.1. The PhET computer simulation "Molecule Shapes."

Your initial task in this activity is to determine the molecule geometry as the number of electron pairs changes. Accomplish this by using **the computer PhET simulation "Molecule Shapes"** and fill in Table 5.2. Start by clicking **"remove all"** and begin with just the central atom.

Notice, in this simulation you can increase the number of electron domains by adding single, double, or triple bonds, or lone pair electrons. In the lower left corner you will find both the molecular geometry and electron geometry. Click on both the Molecule Geometry box and the Electron Geometry box. Click on "Show Bond Angles."

Table 5.2. Model Electron Domain Geometries.

Number of Electron Domains	Electron Domain Geometry	Bond Angles
2	Linear	180°
3		
4		
5		
6		

For Table 5.2, use all single bonds for the additional electron domains.

The molecular geometry is the same as the electron domain geometry **if** all domains contain bonding pairs. If the lone pair electrons are present on the central atom, the molecular geometry will **NOT** be the same as the electron domain geometry. To investigate this, return to the simulation and complete Table 5.3.

Table 5.3. Electron and Molecular Geometries.

Number of Electron Domains	Bonding Pairs	Nonbonding Pairs	Electron Domain Geometry	Molecular Geometry	Sketch an Example
2	2	0			
3	3	0			
3	2	1			
4	4	0			
4	3	1			
4	2	2			
5	5	0			
5	4	1			
5	3	2			
5	2	3			
6	6	0			
6	5	1			
6	4	2			

Question 1. VSEPR stands for "valence-shell electron-pair repulsion." How does electron-pair repulsion determine the molecular geometry? Discuss two specific examples from the table. (Hint: In the simulation is it possible to force the electron domains to be close together?)

NOTES

Question Set 2.

Identify the molecular geometry for each shape.

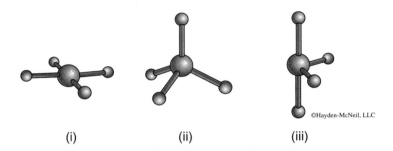

©Hayden-McNeil, LLC

(i)   (ii)   (iii)

    i.

    ii.

    iii.

Determine the electron domain geometry on which the molecular geometry is based.

    i.

    ii.

    iii.

How many lone pairs are on each central atom?

    i.

    ii.

    iii.

You may have noticed that some electron domains appear larger than others. To investigate how the resulting molecular geometry may be affected, complete **Table 5.4** and predict both the geometry and the bond angles. Then, compare your predictions with the experimentally determined bond angles (select **"Real Molecules"**).

Table 5.4. Comparison of Electron Domains.

Molecule	Lewis Structure	Predicted Molecular Geometry	Predicted Bond Angles	Experimentally Determined Bond Angles
NH_3				
H_2O				
SO_2				

Question 3. Which assumption about the space occupied by nonbonding (lone pair) electron pairs is most consistent with the experimental bond angles: do nonbonding pairs occupy more, less, or the same amount of space as bonding pairs?

Activity 3: Molecular Polarity

Using your browser, go to https://phet.colorado.edu/en/simulation/molecule-polarity. Press play.

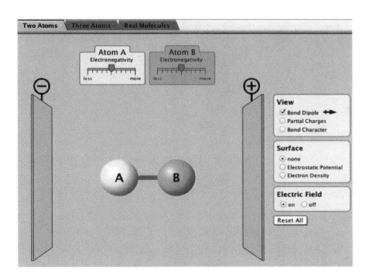

NOTES

Investigating Bond Polarity with the Molecule AB

Select the **"Two Atoms"** tab on the top.

In this simulation you will examine the **bond polarity**, which is a measure of how equally the electrons in a bond are shared between the two atoms of the bond.

There are different ways of representing where the electrons are in a bond. Take a few minutes and try the different "views" in the simulation, i.e., bond dipole, partial charges, and bond character. The electron density or electrostatic potential are other ways of communicating where the electrons are in the molecule.

 Note: Within the simulation you change the relative electronegativity of atoms A and B.

Question Set 4. Use complete sentences to answer the questions below.

Explain how the direction of the arrow in the bond dipole symbol (⊢→) relates to the electron density and the partial charges.

How does changing the electronegativity of the atoms affect the bond polarity?

How does changing the electronegativity of the atoms affect the bond character?

Molecules in Electric Fields

In this simulation the molecule AB is placed between electric plates (–) and (+) and an electric field can be turned on or off. It is also possible to click on the molecule AB and rotate it.

Question Set 5. Use complete sentences to answer the questions below.

What happens to the molecule AB when it has a bond dipole and the electric field is turned on? Spin the molecule around several times and make observations. What if the bond dipole is zero?

Is there a relationship between the magnitude of the bond dipole and how the molecule is affected by the electric field?

NOTES

Investigating Bond Polarity and Molecular Polarity with the Molecule ABC

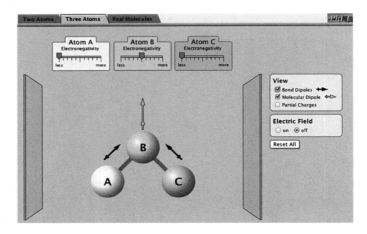

Select the **"Three Atoms"** tab on the top.

In this portion of the simulation you can manipulate molecule ABC. The relative electronegativity of each atom can again be changed. However, it is now also possible to change the geometry by clicking and dragging an atom to change the angle ∠ABC. Once again, you can spin the entire molecule.

In the view section a new option has been added, **"Molecular Dipole."** Molecular polarity describes the charge distribution in the entire molecule, not just a bond. If centers of positive and negative charge do not coincide, the molecule is *polar*. How can you predict if a molecule is polar? The two important variables are 1) the bond dipoles in the molecule, and 2) the molecular geometry.

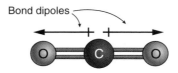

Overall dipole moment = 0

It is important to note that bond dipoles are vector quantities; that is, they have both a magnitude and a direction. In a polyatomic molecule, like ABC, the magnitude and the direction of the individual bond dipoles must be considered when summing vectors. As an example, consider the molecule CO_2. In this molecule there are two bond dipoles because the electronegativity of carbon and oxygen differ. There is no overall molecular dipole, however, because the bond dipoles "cancel" since they are of equal magnitude and pointed in opposite directions. Carbon dioxide is an example of a *nonpolar molecule* that has polar bonds.

To explore the idea of molecular polarity, complete the following table. Make an initial prediction as to whether each ABC molecule will be polar or nonpolar based on the bond dipoles and the geometry; remember, bond dipoles are vector quantities. Then, construct the molecule in the simulation and see how it behaves in the electric field. Were your predictions correct? Add in the bond dipoles, rotate the molecules and observe how the vectors add together, subtract or cancel out. Ignore very, very slight movements.

Molecule	Which atom is most electronegative in the molecule?	PREDICTION: Is the molecule going to be polar or nonpolar?	TEST your molecule in the simulation. Is it affected by the electric field?

Putting It All Together...

Being able to predict the polarity of a molecule is extremely important since many properties of molecules depend on whether they are polar or nonpolar. As you have seen in this activity, determining a molecule's polarity is a multistep process:

1. Draw Lewis structure

2. Use VSEPR to determine molecular geometry

3. Determine bond polarity (based on electronegativity differences)

4. Determine molecular polarity based on bond dipoles and molecular geometry

For the following molecules complete this step-by-step process. Make a prediction, and then check it in the "Real Molecules" section of the simulation. In the simulation you can rotate the molecules. Note how the dipole vectors add together or cancel each other out.

Molecule	Lewis Structure	Molecular Geometry	Is there a molecular dipole? A molecular dipole indicates it is a polar molecule.
N_2			
H_2O			
BF_3			
HCN			
CH_2F_2			
NH_3			
CH_2O			
O_3			
CO_2			

Question Set 6.

What is the difference between molecular geometry and electron geometry?

What information could you determine using a Lewis structure and any other chemistry knowledge that you have? Circle all that may apply.

Hybridization	Elements Present	Reactivity
Types of Bonds	Intermolecular Forces	# of Valence Electrons
Relative Boiling Point	Geometry/Shape	Chemical Properties
Relative Melting Point	Polarity	Potential for Resonance
Bond Angle	Acidity/Basicity	No Information
Formal Charges	# of Bonds Between Atoms	

NOTES

CHAPTER 6

Chemical Kinetics

6

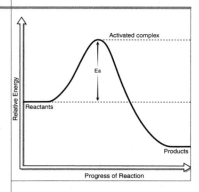

Abstracted in part from: Joseph March and David Shaw, *Discovery and Analysis in The Laboratory*, University of Wisconsin–Madison, 1997.

Purpose

The purpose of this experiment is to use spectrophotometric data to determine the rate law for the reaction between crystal violet and sodium hydroxide.

You will perform several tasks to find the rate law for the reaction between crystal violet and sodium hydroxide. These tasks are listed below:

1. Perform an absorption spectrum for crystal violet to find the wavelength of maximum absorption for crystal violet.

2. Set the spectrometer to zero using a blank or control solution.

3. Prepare a standard curve for crystal violet using four standard solutions of crystal violet.

4. Determine the molar absorptivity of crystal violet for your standard curve.

5. Use the molar absorptivity value and Beer-Lambert law to program Logger *Pro* to calculate the concentration of crystal violet as the dye reacts with sodium hydroxide over time.

6. Measure the concentration of crystal violet over time as it reacts with three different concentrations of sodium hydroxide (0.050 M, 0.075 M and 0.10 M.)

7. Use the data from the reaction of crystal violet with 0.050M sodium hydroxide to construct three graphs: $[CV^+]$ vs. time, $\ln[CV^+]$ vs. time, and $1/[CV^+]$ vs. time. The graph resulting in a straight line will allow you to determine the order of the reaction with respect to CV^+.

8. Find the slope of the line, k_{obs}, for kinetic data generated with each concentration of sodium hydroxide using the same integrated law (i.e., the law that produces a straight line.)

9. Calculate three values for the order of the reaction with respect to sodium hydroxide using Equation 9, your three values of k_{obs} and the corresponding concentrations of sodium hydroxide.

10. Finally, calculate three values for the rate constant, k, using Equation 7, your three values of k_{obs} and the corresponding concentrations of sodium hydroxide.

Introduction

Crystal violet is an organic salt that dissociates in aqueous solution to produce the violet-colored cation, triphenylmethane (CV^+), and a colorless chloride ion. In the presence of a base (e.g., NaOH), the violet-colored cation CV^+ reacts to produce a colorless carbinol base (Equation 1):

$$CV^+ + OH^- \rightleftharpoons CVOH \qquad (1)$$

$$\text{violet} \qquad\qquad \text{colorless}$$

In this experiment, you will use a spectrophotometer to measure the disappearance of the violet-colored CV^+ as it reacts with sodium hydroxide. This instrument measures the absorbance of visible light as it passes through crystal violet. The absorbance of visible light by this colored species is directly related to its concentration. The relationship between concentration and absorbance is known as the Beer-Lambert law and can be expressed by the equation:

$$A = \varepsilon \times \ell \times C$$

or

absorbance = (molar absorptivity) × (path length) × (concentration)   (2)

The spectrophotometer will be interfaced with a computer program that will aid you in producing a standard curve and finding the molar absorptivity for crystal violet. You will then use Beer's law and the molar absorptivity to calculate the concentration of the crystal violet. You will use the integrated rate laws and the plots displayed by the computer to find the order of the reaction.

 Refer to the Spectroscopy section of How to Be Successful in CHM 12901: A Guide to Using Laboratory Equipment and Instrumentation at the beginning of this manual for detailed information about absorption spectra, standard curves, and use of the spectrophotometer.

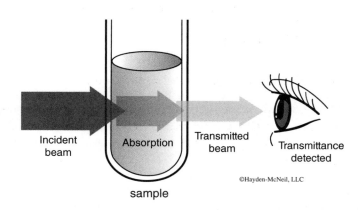

©Hayden-McNeil, LLC

Figure 6.1. Interaction of light with aqueous solutions.

The Rate Law

The rate of a chemical reaction is defined as the change in concentration of either a reactant or product per unit of time. For the reaction between crystal violet cation (CV^+) and hydroxide ion (OH^-), the rate of disappearance of CV^+, the rate of disappearance of OH^-, and the rate of appearance of CVOH are equal because one mole of CVOH is produced for every mole of CV^+ and OH^- that react:

$$\text{rate} = \frac{-\Delta[CV^+]}{\Delta t} = \frac{-\Delta[OH^-]}{\Delta t} = \frac{+\Delta[CVOH]}{\Delta t} \qquad (3)$$

Rates of chemical reactions can depend on several factors, including temperature, concentrations of the reactants, and/or products and the presence of a catalyst. The influence of these variables on a particular chemical reaction must be determined experimentally and is generally expressed in the form of a **rate law**. Although the form of the rate law is specific to a given reaction and can be quite complex, rate laws have the general form:

$$\text{Rate} = k[A]^a[B]^b[C]^c \qquad (4)$$

where k is the **rate constant**, [A], [B], and [C] are the concentrations of each of the reactants in the chemical reaction, and a, b, and c (exponents) represent the order of the reaction with respect to that reactant. For the reaction of crystal violet cation with hydroxide ion (1), the general form of the rate law is:

$$\text{Rate} = k[CV^+]^a[OH^-]^b \qquad (5)$$

Order of Reaction with Respect to CV^+

To quantify the rate of the reaction between CV^+ and OH^-, the orders of each reactant appearing in the rate law (i.e., a and b in Equation 5) must be experimentally determined. This presents an interesting experimental challenge because it becomes necessary to study both [CV^+] and [OH^-] simultaneously. However, if a large excess of OH^- is used, the [OH^-] will remain relatively constant during the course of the reaction and the rate law reduces to:

$$\text{Rate} = k_{obs}[CV^+]^a \qquad (6)$$

substituting this expression into equation 5 results in the following relationship:

$$k_{obs} = k\left[OH^-\right]^b \text{ or } k = \frac{k_{obs}}{\left[OH^-\right]^b} \tag{7}$$

where k_{obs} is the observed or experimental rate constant.

The order of the reaction with respect to CV^+ can be determined by first measuring the concentration of CV^+ as a function of time in a solution containing an excess of OH^-. Then, the experimental data is plotted using each of the three **integrated rate laws**.

Each of the integrated rate laws has the form of a straight (i.e., linear) line. For example, if the reaction between CV^+ and OH^- is zero order with respect to CV^+, a graph of $[CV^+]$ versus time will be linear with a slope equal to $-k_{obs}$. If the reaction is first order with respect to CV^+, a graph of $\ln[CV^+]$ versus time will be linear with a slope equal to $-k_{obs}$. Finally, if the reaction is second order with respect to CV^+, a graph of $1/[CV^+]$ versus time will be linear with a slope equal to k_{obs}.

Table 6.1. Integrated Rate Laws for Zero-, First-, and Second-Order Reactions.

Order	Integrated Rate Law	Plot	Slope
zero (a = 0)	$[CV^+] = -k_{obs}t + [CV^+]_0$	$[CV^+]$ vs. time	$-k_{obs}$
first (a = 1)	$\ln[CV^+] = -k_{obs}t + \ln[CV^+]_0$	$\ln[CV^+]$ vs. time	$-k_{obs}$
second (a = 2)	$\frac{1}{[CV^+]} = k_{obs}t + \frac{1}{[CV^+]_0}$	$\frac{1}{[CV^+]}$ vs. time	k_{obs}

t = time; $[CV^+]$ = concentration of CV^+ at time t; $[CV^+]_0$ = initial concentration of CV^+

The experimental data must be plotted using all three integrated laws. You will construct these graphs in Logger *Pro*. Only one of the three graphs will be linear (the other two will be curved).

Order of Reaction with Respect to OH⁻

To determine the order of the reaction with respect to OH^-, it is necessary to study the reaction at (at least) two different initial concentrations of OH^- *at the same temperature*. Equation 7 can be used to derive an expression that relates the experimentally determined rate constants, k_{obs}, for the two initial concentrations of OH^-:

$$\frac{k_{obs2}}{k_{obs1}} = \frac{k\left[OH^-\right]_2^b}{k\left[OH^-\right]_1^b} = \left(\frac{\left[OH^-\right]_2}{\left[OH^-\right]_1}\right)^b \tag{8}$$

Taking the natural logarithm of both sides of Equation 8 and rearranging gives:

$$b = \frac{\ln(k_{obs2}) - \ln(k_{obs1})}{\ln[OH^-]_2 - \ln[OH^-]_1} \qquad (9)$$

One can then calculate b from the slope of the linear graph and the $[OH^-]$.

Prelab

As part of your individual preparation for lab, read the experiment and answer the following questions in your lab notebook before going to lab. The copy of your answers on perforated pages from your lab notebook is due at the beginning of lab.

1. Write the relationship between the rate of disappearance of $H_2C_2O_4(aq)$ and the rate of appearance of $Mn^{2+}(aq)$ for the reaction represented by the following equation:

$2\,MnO_4^-(aq) + 5\,H_2C_2O_4(aq) + 6\,H_3O^+(aq) \rightarrow 10\,CO_2(g) + 2\,Mn^{2+}(aq) + 14\,H_2O(\ell)$

2. Why do you measure the disappearance of reactant (crystal violet) and not the appearance of product in this experiment?

3. In your laboratory notebook, record the experimental procedure you will follow in lab. The procedure is your experimental plan and can be organized as an outline, a flowchart, or a numbered list of steps. You should also include a statement of the purpose of the experiment, notes on safety, and a reference to the relevant pages in your laboratory manual. The copy of your procedure on the duplicate pages of your lab notebook is due at the beginning of lab.

Absorption Spectrum, Standard Curve, and Determining the Rate Law

Your group will first find the wavelength of maximum absorption for crystal violet. After setting the spectrophotometer to this optimum wavelength, you will construct a standard curve for crystal violet. Four standard solutions of crystal violet will be provided. The exact concentration of the standards will be listed on the bottles.

Your group will then determine the rate law for the reaction of crystal violet with hydroxide ion at room temperature using three different concentrations of OH^-.

0.050 M NaOH in 50% ethanol

0.075 M NaOH in 50% ethanol

0.10 M NaOH in 50% ethanol

You will be borrowing a special glass cuvette from your teaching assistant for this experiment. Handle the cuvette with care. Return the cuvette to your teaching assistant when you are finished.

Data Collection

Lab work is done in groups. Each person must (1) record a complete set of data for standards in his/her lab notebook and (2) turn in the duplicate copy on the perforated pages from the lab notebook at the end of lab with the group report.

Waste

Collect all solutions containing crystal violet in a beaker on your benchtop. This collected solution can be discarded down the drain with plenty of water.

Procedure

Connect the SpectroVis Spectrophotometer

1. Start the Logger *Pro* application.

2. Connect the SpectroVis spectrophotometer to the computer with the USB-B cable.

The above instructions must be performed in order. If you do not see a color spectrum in Logger *Pro*, disconnect the spectrometer, close the program and try again.

Calibrate the Vernier SpectroVis Plus with the Blank

Before the absorption spectrum of crystal violet can be measured, it is necessary to obtain an absorption spectrum for the blank solution. In this case the blank is 50% ethanol. All solutions of crystal violet and sodium hydroxide used in this experiment were prepared in 50% ethanol.

A blank correction scan or calibration is used to correct for any absorbance by the solvent, impurities or irregularities in the optics of the instrument, etc. The absorbance of the blank solution will be measured over the entire wavelength range. The resulting absorbance versus wavelength data will be stored internally. When the absorption spectrum of a sample (such as crystal violet) is subsequently measured, the absorption of the blank solution will be subtracted from the absorbance of the sample solution at each wavelength.

1. Rinse the cuvette by rolling a small amount of 50% ethanol in the cuvette. Discard the rinse into a waste beaker.

2. Fill a cuvette at least 1/3 full with the blank solution. Wipe the outside of the cuvette with a Kimwipe.

3. From the **Experiment** menu, choose **Calibrate > Spectrometer: 1.**

4. The calibration dialog box will display the message: "Waiting 90 seconds for lamp to warm up."

5. When warmup is complete, place the cuvette in the sample chamber of the SpectroVis.

6. Click **Finish Calibration**.

7. Click **OK**.

Absorption Spectrum for Crystal Violet to Find the Wavelength of Maximum Absorption

For quantitative measurements, it is preferable to choose a wavelength of light that is near the maximum absorbance, λ_{max}, for the compound of interest. The λ_{max} is found by measuring the compound's absorbance spectrum over a range of wavelengths.

1. Click ▮ (**Configure Spectrometer**).

2. Select **Absorbance vs. Wavelength** as the **Collection Mode**. Click **OK**.

3. Rinse and fill a cuvette at least 1/3 full with crystal violet standard 3. Discard the rinse into a waste jar. Wipe cuvette with a Kimwipe.

4. Place the cuvette in the sample chamber of the SpectroVis and click ▶ **Collect** .

5. Wait 10 seconds.

6. An absorption spectrum of crystal violet will appear in a Logger *Pro* window.

7. Click ▮▮ **Stop** to end data collection.

From the absorption spectrum of crystal violet, determine the best wavelength for measuring the absorbance of crystal violet by looking for the maximum absorbance in the table or by clicking ▦ **Examine** and placing the cursor on the peak. Record this wavelength, λ_{max}, in your lab notebook and make all absorption measurements of the standards and samples at this wavelength.

8. Print the spectrum and include the graph in your report. Make sure the title and axes are labeled.

9. You can save the graph as a .cmbl file that can only be used with Logger *Pro* by clicking **File > Save As**.... The Logger *Pro* program is available in iTAP laboratories.

You can also save the data to use in a spreadsheet program such as Excel. There are two methods listed below.

Method 1

Copy and paste the data:

1. Select the data in the Logger *Pro* table.

2. Choose Copy from the Edit menu.

3. Switch to Excel and paste the data into the Excel sheet.

Method 2

Export the data from Logger *Pro* to a file that can be opened in a spreadsheet program:

1. Choose Export As from the File menu.

2. Select CSV as the export file type.

3. Name and save the file.

This file can be opened in most spreadsheet programs, such as Microsoft Excel, OpenOffice, or Google Docs.

Standard Curve for Crystal Violet

The molar absorptivity value will be used to calculate the crystal violet concentration during the kinetics reactions. You must keep a record of the concentrations and corresponding absorbance values for all the standard solutions in addition to the molar absorptivity and cuvette path length in your lab notebook.

1. Click , **Configure Spectrometer.**

2. Select **Absorbance vs. Concentration** as the collection mode.

3. Change the **Column Name** to "Concentration," the **Short Name** to "conc," and the **Units** to mol/L.

4. Click on the wavelength to use for absorbance measurements, the wavelength of maximum absorbance, or λ_{max} then click **OK**.

5. When ready to collect absorbance-concentration data for the crystal violet standards, click . The program will prompt you to store the latest run (the spectrum). Check that the spectrum data is saved, then choose do not store latest run. When asked, do not store the latest run or spectrum.

6. For each of the four standards, in order from the least concentrated (1) to the most concentrated (4), do the following.

    a. Rinse (with the standard solution) and fill the cuvette at least 1/3 full with the standard solution. Wipe the cuvette with a Kimwipe.

   b.   Insert the cuvette into the spectrophotometer.

   c.   Wait 10 seconds, press 🔘 **Keep** , type the concentration in exponential notation (i.e., 1.23E-4) into the edit box, and press **Enter**.

   d.   Record the absorbance of the standard in your lab notebook.

7.   After two data points have been recorded click **⒜ Autoscale**.

8.   After you have recorded the absorbance of all four standards, click **◼ Stop** .

You may save or transfer this information to an Excel spreadsheet at this time and prepare the standard curve using Excel. If you would prefer to use Logger *Pro* to prepare the standard curve, the instructions follow.

A standard curve of the absorbance versus concentration for the standards should be visible. Click on ▨, the **Linear Fit** button, to find the equation of the best-fit straight line and display the equation on the graph. The equation of the line corresponds to Equation 2 in your lab manual.

Record the molar absorptivity, ε, in your lab notebook.

9.   Print the standard curve and include the graph in your report. Make sure the title and axes are labeled.

10. Save the data. Give the calibration curve data a different file name. Do not overwrite spectrum data.

Determining the Order of the Reaction with Respect to CV⁺ at Room Temperature

To determine the order of reaction with respect to CV^+, you will collect kinetic data for the reaction at room temperature with 0.050 M NaOH in 50% ethanol.

1.   Click 🖿, **Configure Spectrophotometer**.

2.   Select **Absorbance vs. Time** as the collection mode.

3.   Click on the wavelength corresponding to the λ_{max} then click **OK**.

4.   Make sure that the calibration curve data has been saved. When asked, do not store the latest run.

Before you begin, adjust the attributes of the graph. Right-click anywhere on the graph and choose **Graph Options**. Change the appearance of the graph by selecting **point symbols** and deselecting **connect points**.

You will also want the program to calculate the concentration of the crystal violet. Follow the directions below to perform the calculation.

5.   From the **Data** menu choose **New Calculated Column**.

6.   As the **Name**, enter "Concentration," conc as the **Short Name,** and **M** for the unit.

7. Place the cursor in the **Expression** edit box. From the **Variables** list select "**Absorbance**," divide by your molar absorptivity by typing /ε, where ε is the molar absorptivity determined earlier from your calibration plot. For example, if you found that the molar absorptivity is $5.00 \times 10^8 \, \mathrm{L/cm^{-1}mol^{-1}}$, you would enter "Absorbance"/5.00E8.

8. Change the number of significant digits by selecting the **Options** tab and set the **Displayed Precision** to two decimal places. Next, check the box for scientific notation. Click **Done**.

9. Click on the y-axis label. Choose **Concentration**.

When you are ready to run a reaction:

10. Rinse a cuvette with a small amount of 0.050 M NaOH solution, then fill the cuvette with about 7 mL (80% full) of the 0.050 M NaOH solution. Have a small piece of Parafilm ready to cover the cuvette.

11. Add one drop of the 5×10^{-3} M crystal violet solution to the NaOH in the cuvette.

    Quickly cover the cuvette with a piece of Parafilm, and invert the cuvette twice to mix.

12. Wipe the outside of the cuvette and insert it into the spectrophotometer.

13. Click ▶ **Collect**.

14. Click **A** **Autoscale**.

15. Collect data until the curve flattens and the absorbance approaches zero. Click **Stop** to terminate the data collection.

16. Save the data. Give the data a unique file name. Do not overwrite previous data.

17. After the data has been saved, click **Data > Clear All Data**.

Determine Order of OH⁻ Using Room Temperature Data

To determine the order of the OH⁻ you will need kinetic data for three different concentrations of NaOH: 0.050 M, 0.075 M, and 0.10 M.

1. You have collected data for the reaction of crystal violet and 0.050 M sodium hydroxide; now collect data for the reaction of crystal violet with 0.075 M and 0.10 M sodium hydroxide. Rinse the cuvette with appropriate concentration of NaOH and repeat the reaction of crystal violet concentration versus time at room temperature with 0.075 M NaOH and 0.10 M NaOH.

2. Save your data. Give the data a unique file name. Do not overwrite previous data.

Cleanup

Disconnect the spectrophotometer and return it to the box on your bench. Rinse the cuvette with deionized water. Return the cuvette to the instructor.

Wait for the waste collected in a beaker to become colorless, and then pour the solution down the drain with water.

Rinse all glassware with deionized water.

Data Analysis/Calculations

Remove Invalid Data Points

Toward the end of the reaction between CV^+ and OH^-, the concentration of the product (CVOH) is sufficiently high that the reverse reaction competes with the forward reaction. Because we are trying to measure the rate of the forward reaction only, it is necessary to ignore the data points toward the end of the reaction.

Construct a graph by plotting concentration versus time (Logger *Pro* or Excel) using your experimental data. Examine the graph and note the time at which the bottom of the curve begins to flatten out. Remove all data points to the right of this value (see the figure below).

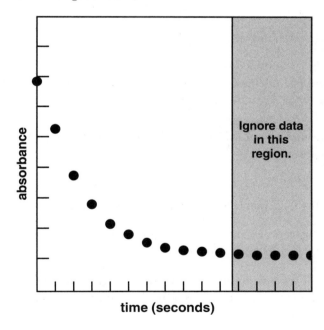

Figure 6.2. Select valid data points.

Removing Invalid Data Points in Logger *Pro*

1. Select data points that correspond to a flattening out of the graph as it approaches zero. You can select the data by dragging the cursor over the points on the graph or table.

2. From the **Edit** menu select **Strike Through Data Cells** to exclude from calculations.

3. Save the changes.

4. Repeat this for all three sets of data.

Determine Order of CV⁺ Using Room Temperature Data

Using your group's 0.050 M NaOH data, you will identify which of the following graphs

$[CV^+]$ versus time or $\ln[CV^+]$ versus time or $1/[CV^+]$ versus time

represent a linear relationship.

Construct a plot of $[CV^+]$ versus time, $\ln[CV^+]$ versus time, and $1/[CV^+]$ versus time using the data collected for the reaction of crystal violet and 0.050 M NaOH. See directions below for constructing these plots in Logger *Pro*.

Examine each graph and identify the function that results in a straight line after you have omitted data from the flat region of the $[CV^+]$ versus time graph. Remember each of the integrated rate laws has the form of a straight line, in other words, produces a linear relationship. See Table 6.1 in your lab manual.

Sketch each graph in your notebook.

Once you have identified which plot is linear, you will determine the slope of that straight line to obtain a value for the observed rate constant, k_{obs}. Attach the graphs to the report form as documentation of your experimental results.

Constructing Plots of ln[CV⁺] versus Time and 1/[CV⁺] versus Time Using Logger Pro

$\ln[CV^+]$ versus time

1. From the **Data** menu choose **New Calculated Column**.

2. Enter "ln Concentration" as the **Name**, "ln Conc" as the **Short Name**, and leave the unit blank.

3. Enter the formula for the column into the **Expressions** edit box. From the **Function** list select **ln**, and from the **Variables** list selecting "Concentration." Click **Done**.

4. Click on the y-axis label. Choose **ln Concentration**. A graph of ln concentration vs. time should now be displayed. Change the scale of the graph, if necessary, by clicking ▲ **Autoscale**.

$1/[CV^+]$ versus time

1. From the **Data** menu choose **New Calculated Column**.

2. Enter "1/Concentration" as the **Name**, "1/Conc" as the **Short Name**, and leave the unit blank.

3. Enter the formula for the column into the **Expressions** edit box. To do this, type in "1" and "/." Then from the **Variables** list select "Concentration." Click **Done**.

4. Click on the y-axis label. Choose **1/Concentration**. A graph of 1/Concentration vs. time should now be displayed. Change the scale of the graph, if necessary, by clicking 📊 **Autoscale**.

Determine Value of k_{obs} for Different Concentrations of OH⁻ at Room Temperature

Construct separate graphs using the 0.050 M, 0.075 M, and 0.10 M NaOH data and the plotting method that you found provides a linear graph of the 0.050 M NaOH experimental data. Make sure you ignore the invalid data points. Print the equation for the trendline on each graph.

Determine the value of the rate constant, k_{obs}, for each OH⁻ concentration from the slope of the line. Attach an appropriately labeled graph for each concentration of NaOH to your lab report (3 graphs).

Calculate Order of OH⁻ at Room Temperature

Calculate three values for the order of the reaction with respect to OH⁻ using Equation 9, and your values for k_{obs1}, k_{obs2}, and k_{obs3}. Calculate an average value for the order of the reaction with respect to OH⁻. Round the computed average value to the nearest integer.

Calculate Value of Rate Constant, k, at Room Temperature

Calculate three values for the rate constant, k, at room temperature using Equation 7, your values for k_{obs1}, k_{obs2}, and k_{obs3} with corresponding OH⁻ concentrations, and the order of the reaction (rounded to nearest integer) with respect to OH⁻. Calculate an average value for the rate constant, k, at room temperature.

Results

Write the chemical equation that represents the chemical reaction being studied, along with your experimentally determined rate law.

Postlab Questions

General Questions

1. Students were studying decomposition reactions to determine how the rate of the reaction could be described and understood mathematically. The reactions were identified as reaction 33 and reaction 15. General profiles of various graphs of the data are as follows.

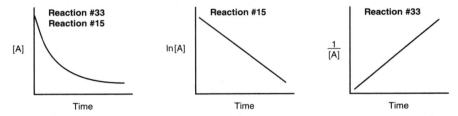

    Write the integrated rate law that would be used to describe and calculate the relationships between the concentration of A and time for each of the reactions.

2. Use the following experimental data and a graphing program such as Excel to determine the order of the reaction with respect to $[Cr(NH_3)_5Cl]^{2+}$ and the value of the rate constant, k. Note that OH^- is in excess in this experiment.

    $$[Cr(NH_3)_5Cl]^{2+}(aq) + OH^-(aq) \rightarrow [Cr(NH_3)_5(OH)]^{2+}(aq) + Cl^-(aq)$$

    You must show your work for any calculations. Print your 3 graphs with equations of the trendlines and R^2 values shown. Attach these graphs to your postlab.

Time, min	$[Cr(NH_3)_5Cl]^{2-}$, M
0	1.500
5	0.986
10	0.648
15	0.426
20	0.279
25	0.183
30	0.121

3. To determine the order of OH^- in the reaction with crystal violet, the reaction must be studied using two different initial concentrations of OH^-. Why is it important that all the reactions be done at the same temperature?

Questions from Experiment

4. Explain why you repeated the reaction using three different concentrations of OH⁻.

5. Explain why it was important to remove the invalid data points before fitting a line to your data.

6. What experimental condition allowed you to determine the order of the reaction with respect to CV^+ even though both $[CV^+]$ and $[OH^-]$ are part of the rate law?

NOTES

Lab Records and Reports

Group Portion
Remember that it is your responsibility as a group to ensure that everyone whose name is on the report has participated as fully as possible in the completion of the project.

Individual Portion
Each student must attach laboratory notebook duplicate pages containing a complete data set and observations for the experiment.

NOTES

CHAPTER 7

Enzyme Kinetics: Assaying Acid Phosphatase

7

Objectives

- Learn how to conduct an enzyme assay to quantify the activity of an enzyme.

- Understand the concepts of Michaelis-Menten kinetics.

- Measure the V_{max} of the enzyme wheat germ acid phosphatase and calculate its K_m for the substrate p-nitrophenyl phosphate.

- Quantify the effect of a competitive inhibitor, sodium phosphate, on the enzymatic activity of wheat germ acid phosphatase.

You will perform several tasks to quantify the activity of Wheat Germ Phosphatase and the effect of an inhibitor on this activity. These tasks are listed below:

1. Prepare p-nitrophenol standards.

2. Set the spectrophotometer to a wavelength of 405 nm.

3. Zero the spectrophotometer and measure standards.

4. Prepare eight concentrated substrate cocktails (A–H) of varying concentration of substrate.

5. Transfer 450 µL of each cocktail into 3 tubes.

6. Perform assay of enzyme.

7. Measure absorbance of each assay sample.

8. Prepare eight concentrated substrate cocktails (A–H) of varying concentration of substrate + sodium phosphate inhibitor.

9. Transfer 450 µL of each cocktail into 3 tubes.

10. Perform assay of inhibited enzyme.

NOTES

11. Measure absorbance of each assay sample.

12. Prepare standard curve for *p*-nitrophenol.

13. Calculate the molar absorptivity of *p*-nitrophenol from trendline.

14. Calculate concentration of *p*-nitrophenol in assay samples using Beer's Law.

15. Generate two graphs: 1) Michaelis-Menton and 2) Lineweaver-Burk for the enzyme and inhibited enzyme.

16. Calculate V_{max} and K_m for enzyme and inhibited enzyme from each graph.

Introduction

Every cell must carry out and regulate many essential chemical reactions simultaneously. **Enzymes** catalyze nearly all of these chemical reactions. Unlike inorganic catalysts, which are relatively nonspecific and usually require high temperatures to function, enzymes are specific and work at temperatures that are compatible with life. Their high degree of specificity means that each cell must make hundreds of enzymes to catalyze all of the necessary reactions.

Most enzymes are **proteins** and their activity is a direct consequence of their structure. Proteins are polymers of amino acids held in a three-dimensional shape or **conformation** by numerous, weak (although collectively strong) non-covalent bonds (hydrogen bonds, ionic bonds, hydrophobic interactions, and van der Waals forces). This aspect of their structure makes them flexible—a requirement for their function. Although their structure may change slightly during reactions, they return to their original state after each reaction.

Molecules on which enzymes act are called **substrates**, a term equivalent to reactant. Substrates bind to enzymes at **active sites** that are often in a pocket or cleft in the surface of the protein. Once the substrate is bound, the enzyme catalyzes a chemical reaction resulting in the conversion of the substrate(s) to **product(s)** that then diffuse away from the enzyme. The rate of these reactions, on a per enzyme basis, is often staggering—some enzymes catalyze hundreds of thousands of reactions per second! Controlling the rates of these enzymatic reactions is extremely important to cells.

Enzyme assays are used to measure the activity of a particular enzyme. One common method to conduct an assay is to mix the enzyme with its particular substrate(s) and then quantify the product of the reaction after a predetermined period of time. The amount of product formed per unit time of reaction is the rate of the reaction. Reaction rates are useful for determining the amount of an enzyme in a solution or how its activity is affected by various factors such as pH, temperature, or an inhibitor. In this experiment, you will measure the activity of the enzyme acid phosphatase derived from wheat germ.

One of the substrates that acid phosphatase acts on is called *p*-nitrophenyl phosphate (PNP). After hydrolyzing the phosphate group from the substrate, two products are formed: *p*-nitrophenol and an inorganic phosphate, Pi (see Figure 7.1). Unlike the colorless substrate, *p*-nitrophenol (PN) is a bright yellow compound and is thus convenient to quantify using spectrophotometric analysis. The color of the *p*-nitrophenol is intensified by the addition of sodium hydroxide. The sodium hydroxide also serves to make the enzyme inactive and stop the assay.

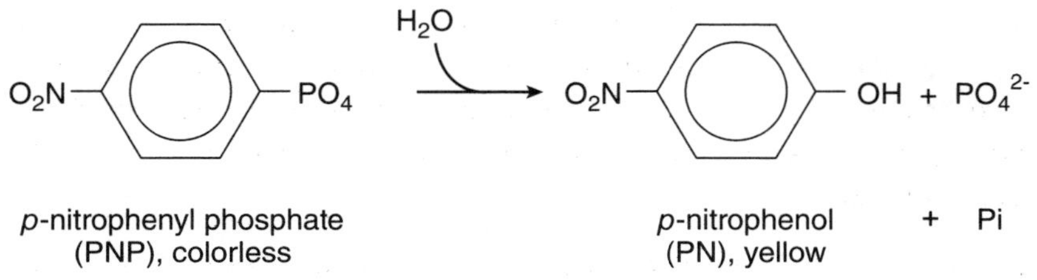

Figure 7.1. Hydrolysis of colorless PNP to yellow PN and inorganic phosphate (Pi).

Unlike studies of whole organisms or ecosystems in which phenomena can often be seen and measured directly, cellular processes can rarely be observed with the naked eye so they cannot be measured directly. To quantify reactions we often design experiments in which a color change takes place since the concentration of colored solutions can be accurately measured using a **spectrophotometer**. In Part I, you will prepare a standard curve for *p*-nitrophenol, the colored product of the acid phosphatase catalyzed reaction. This plot will allow you to monitor the amount of PN produced as acid phosphatase catalyzes the reaction. It will be helpful to review the spectroscopy information in How to Be Successful in CHM 12901: A Guide to Using Laboratory Equipment and Instrumentation at the beginning of this manual.

Michaelis-Menten Enzyme Kinetics

In a cell, as in a test tube, the probability of a reaction occurring is determined by the concentrations of the enzyme and its substrate(s). When the concentrations of enzyme and/or substrate(s) are increased, the probability of collisions between them is higher and as a result the rate of activity increases.

The kinetic model of a single substrate, irreversible enzymatic reaction can be written using the following equation:

$$E + S \xrightleftharpoons[k_{-1}]{k_1} ES \xrightarrow{k_2} E + P$$

where E = free enzyme

S = free substrate

ES = enzyme–substrate complex

P = product

k_n = rate constants

NOTES

At very low substrate concentrations, most of the E will be free while at very high substrate concentrations most of the enzyme will be bound to S, as the enzyme–substrate complex, ES. Three processes affect the rate of activity and are signified by rate constants in the equation: the probability of ES formation (k_1), the reverse reaction of ES disassociation (k_{-1}), and the rate of catalysis or EP to E + P, (k_2). At very low substrate concentrations, the formation of ES will be slow because of the low probability of collisions between E and S. In these situations S is said to be the rate-limiting factor. At very high substrate concentrations most of the E will be bound to S and the rate of activity will be limited by the catalysis of ES to E + P. In these situations E is saturated with S and increasing the concentration of S any further will have no effect on the rate of a reaction.

One other important factor that affects ES formation is the **affinity** of the enzyme for its substrate. The shape of the enzyme's substrate binding site and the number of non-covalent bonds that hold E and S together determine the affinity of an enzyme for its substrate. An enzyme with an open, shallow binding site and many potential sites for non-covalent bond formation will have a higher affinity for the substrate than one with a narrow, deep binding site and fewer sites for non-covalent bonds. With an open binding site, substrate molecules can conceivably approach at a variety of angles and successfully bind, thus increasing the probability of a reaction at a given substrate concentration. By analogy, think of catching a baseball with a glove versus bare-handed. With a glove the probability of catching a fly ball is increased. Similarly, first basemen use extra large gloves to make the probability of catching the ball even higher! Enzymes with a high affinity for a substrate are more likely to be in the ES conformation at a low concentration of S because they bind to S more efficiently than an enzyme with a low affinity for S. Enzymes with a low affinity for a substrate require higher concentrations of S to function efficiently.

The work of Michaelis and Menten allows us to see the relationship between affinity and the rate of the enzymatic reaction. The researchers found that if the rate of the enzymatic reaction is measured over a range of substrate concentrations, [S], the reaction rate or velocity, V, increases as [S] increases (see Figure 7.2). However, as [S] increases, the enzyme becomes saturated with substrate and the rate reaches V_{max}, the enzyme's maximum velocity.

NOTES

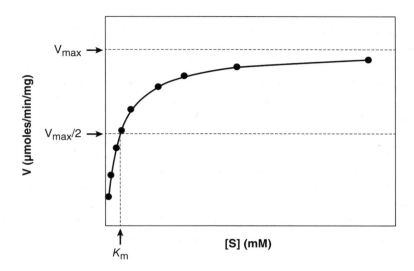

Figure 7.2. Sample plot of the rate of an enzyme's activity (V) expressed as µmoles/min/mg protein, versus the concentration of substrate ([S]) expressed as millimoles/L (mM). The estimated maximum velocity (V_{max}) and Michaelis-Menten constant K_m = [S] at ½ V_{max} are indicated.

Michaelis and Menten derived an equation to describe the enzyme-catalyzed reaction represented in the figure above. The equation is called the Michaelis-Menten equation:

$$V = \frac{V_{max}[S]}{K_m + [S]}$$

V is the reaction velocity, expressed as amount of product produced per unit time.

where $$K_m = \frac{k_{-1} + k_2}{k_1}$$

The affinity of an enzyme for its substrate is represented by the Michaelis-Menten constant or K_m, where the K_m of an enzyme for its substrate is defined as the concentration of substrate at which the rate of reaction (also termed velocity or V) is half the highest possible or maximum rate (V_{max}). Interestingly, enzymes are often exposed to concentrations of substrate that are near the K_m value. This is advantageous to cells because they can regulate reaction rates with relatively small changes in the concentration of S. Remember that K_m and affinity are inversely related. An enzyme with a lower K_m would have a higher affinity for its substrate.

To measure a K_m for a particular enzyme and substrate, one must measure the rate of a reaction at different concentrations of substrate below and above the K_m value. Under ideal conditions, the rate of the reaction should increase with increasing [S] until the enzyme is saturated. At this point increasing the concentration of substrate further will not result in a faster rate of reaction. This is the maximum velocity or V_{max} of the enzyme. In reality, V_{max} can never be attained; it can only be approached. From a V versus [S] curve one can estimate V_{max} and K_m (Figure 7.2).

NOTES

Estimates of V_{max} and K_m from a V versus [S] plot are often inaccurate because the estimates are usually influenced strongly by relatively few data points. More accurate measurements of V_{max} and K_m can be obtained if all of the data points are used. One way to utilize all of the data points is to construct a **Lineweaver-Burk plot** in which the inverse of the rate of the reaction (1/V) is plotted against the inverse of the substrate concentration (1/[S]). If the enzyme displays "Michaelis-Menten Kinetics," all of the data points should fall on a straight line. A linear regression or a trendline can then be used to determine the x- and y-intercepts. The y-intercept is the inverse of V_{max} and the x-intercept is the negative of the inverse of K_m (Figure 7.3). In Part II, you will be estimating and measuring the V_{max} of wheat germ acid phosphatase and its K_m for the substrate *p*-nitrophenyl phosphate by measuring the rate of the catalyzed reaction at different substrate concentrations. You will use the experimental values of V to prepare graphs similar to Figures 7.2 and 7.3.

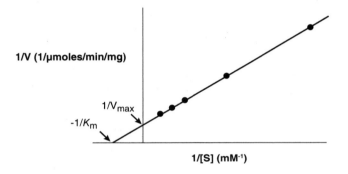

Figure 7.3. Sample Lineweaver-Burk plot. The inverse of the rate of an enzyme's activity (1 µmoles/min/mg) is plotted against the inverse of the concentration of substrate (1/[S], expressed as mM⁻¹). The maximum velocity (V_{max}) is obtained from the y-intercept and the Michaelis-Menten constant (K_m) is obtained from the x-intercept as indicated.

Inhibition of Enzyme Activity

Enzyme inhibitors are molecules that interact with an enzyme to prevent it from working in the normal manner. There are several types of inhibitors, including irreversible and reversible. Two classes of reversible inhibitors are called competitive and noncompetitive inhibitors. Many pharmaceutical drugs are examples of enzyme inhibitors.

A **competitive inhibitor** is any compound that resembles the chemical structure and molecular geometry of the substrate. The inhibitor competes for the same active site as the substrate molecule. The inhibitor may interact with the enzyme at the active site, but no reaction takes place. The inhibitor cannot be converted to product and prevents any substrate molecules from reacting with the enzyme. However, a competitive inhibition is usually reversible if sufficient substrate molecules are available to ultimately displace the inhibitor. Therefore, the amount of enzyme inhibition depends upon the inhibitor concentration, substrate concentration, and the relative affinities of the inhibitor and substrate for the active site.

A **noncompetitive inhibitor** is a substance that interacts with the enzyme, but usually not at the active site. The net effect of a noncompetitive inhibitor is to change the shape of the enzyme and thus the active site, so that the substrate can no longer interact with the enzyme to give a reaction. Noncompetitive inhibitors are usually reversible, but are not influenced by concentrations of the substrate, since it binds in a different location than the substrate.

You will be examining how the addition of a competitive inhibitor affects the activity of wheat germ acid phosphatase and how the values of K_m and V_{max} are affected.

Prelab

Answer the following questions in your lab notebook before going to lab. The copy of your answers on perforated pages from your lab notebook is due at the beginning of lab.

1. If one mole of substance X is dissolved in 1.00 L of water, what is the concentration of the solution in molarity (M)?

   If one mole of substance X is dissolved in 500 mL of water (0.500 L), what is the concentration of the solution?

   If one mole of substance X is dissolved in 2.00 L of water, what is the concentration of the solution?

2. If a 500-mL solution containing 500 millimoles of substance X is a 1.00 M solution, how many moles would be in 100 mL of the solution?

   What would be the molarity of that 100-mL solution?

   How many millimoles would be dissolved in 1 milliliter (mL) of the solution?

   What would be the molarity of a solution containing 10 mL of the 1.00 M solution added to 10 mL of water?

3. For the enzyme assays you will be conducting, what are the names of the enzyme, substrate, and products of the reaction?

Enzyme = _____

Substrate = _____

Product = _____

How will the rate of reaction be monitored? Which of the above components will be measured and how?

4. A standard curve is needed to determine the concentration of the product of the enzyme activity. A stock solution of 2.00×10^{-4} M p-nitrophenol (PN), the product of the enzymatic reaction, will be provided. You will prepare six standard solutions of the PN at concentrations ranging from 4.00×10^{-6} M to 8.00×10^{-5} M. Fill in Table 7.1, given 2.00×10^{-4} M p-nitrophenol (PN) stock solution. Each dilution of stock should have a total volume of 1000 µL. Use $C_1 V_1 = C_2 V_2$ where C is concentration (M) and V is volume in µL.

Table 7.1. Preparing Dilutions of PN.

Tube #	C_2, Final [PN] in M	V_2, Final Volume in µL	V_1, Volume of 2.00×10^{-4} M Stock PN in µL	Volume of Water in µL $(1000 \ µL - V_1)$
0 (blank)	0	1000 µL		
1	4.00×10^{-6}	1000 µL		
2	1.00×10^{-5}	1000 µL		
3	2.00×10^{-5}	1000 µL		
4	4.00×10^{-5}	1000 µL		
5	5.00×10^{-5}	1000 µL		
6	8.00×10^{-5}	1000 µL		

For the standard curve, the above solutions are diluted further before the absorbance is measured with the spectrophotometer. You are instructed to add 1000 µL of 0.5 M NaOH for a total volume of 2000 µL. Calculate the final concentration of PN (**in M or moles/L**) of these solutions and record in Table 7.2.

Table 7.2. Final Concentration of *p*-nitrophenol for Standard Curve.

Test Tube	[PN] (M) after NaOH is Added
0	
1	
2	
3	
4	
5	
6	

5. In this course and future courses you will need to know how to prepare solutions. Rather than prepare each solution starting from dry chemicals, one makes stock solutions that are, for convenience, 10 times more concentrated than the final concentration one desires. These are called 10× stock solutions. When diluting a 10× stock solution, one mixes one-tenth of the desired final volume as 10× stock and then adds deionized H_2O to the desired final volume.

    Example: To make a 5 mL solution of 20 mM "Q," one would first make a solution of 200 mM "Q" (the 10× stock) and then combine 0.5 mL of 10× Q with 4.5 mL of deionized H_2O.

    To make a 50 mL solution of 1 M "T," one would first prepare a 10× solution with a concentration of _____ (M) T. You would then combine _____ mL of 10× T with _____ (mL) of deionized H_2O.

6. Calculate the specific activity of an enzyme in μmol/min/mg of protein assuming that you used 50 μL of enzyme at 0.3 mg/mL (equivalent to 0.3 μg/μL so 50 μL will contain 15 μg) in a 10-minute assay and obtained an absorbance value of 0.810 in a 1 cm tube. The product of the reaction was found to have a molar absorptivity, ε, of 1.84×10^4 $M^{-1}cm^{-1}$. The total volume of the assay is 1.5 mL.

    We have provided a road map to assist you with this calculation.

    0.810 absorption units/1.84×10^4 $M^{-1}cm^{-1}$ = _____ mol/L (mmol/mL)

    _____ mmol/mL × 1.5 mL   = _____ mmol

    _____ mmol × 1000 μmol/mmol   = _____ μmol

    _____ μmol/10 minutes   = _____ μmol/min

    _____ μmol/min/15 μg protein   = _____ μmol/min/μg protein

    _____ μmol/min/μg × 1000 μg/mg   = _____ μmol/min/mg protein

NOTES

7. When the concentration of substrate [S] is very high the enzyme is said to be _____ with substrate. Briefly describe what this indicates about the state of the enzyme (i.e., free, bound to the substrate, or bound to the product).

8. What is the definition of K_m? In what units is K_m expressed?

9. What is a Lineweaver-Burk plot and what is its purpose?

10. Complete Tables 7.4, 7.5, and 7.8.

11. In your laboratory notebook, record the experimental procedure you will follow in lab. The procedure is your experimental plan and can be organized as an outline, a flowchart, or a numbered list of steps. You should also include a statement of the purpose of the experiment, notes on safety, and a reference to the relevant pages in your laboratory manual. The copy of your procedure on the duplicate pages of your lab notebook is due at the beginning of lab.

Procedure

Lab work is done in groups of three or four. Each person must record a complete set of data. Each person will turn in the duplicate copy of the data on the perforated page from his/her lab notebook at the end of the lab in addition to the group report.

NOTES

Disposable, glass test tubes will be provided for this assay. Please discard all solutions into the appropriate waste jar and dispose of all test tubes in the "glass trash" receptacles.

Reagents

Each group will be given all of the reagents needed to complete the experiment in vials, with the exception of 0.50 M NaOH. The 0.50 M NaOH will be on the reagent bench. Your teaching assistant will provide the reagents. Place the vials of *p*-nitrophenol and 10× buffer in one of the cardboard boxes provided. The wheat germ acid phosphatase (enzyme) and *p*-nitrophenyl phosphate (substrate) must be kept on ice. Place these vials in a small beaker of ice.

 NOTE: The enzyme and substrate must be thawed and mixed well before dispensing. The solutions should thaw on ice. If you see ice in the solutions, briefly warm the vial with your hand while inverting the vial to mix.

Equipment

You will also need the following:

1. A Genesys spectrophotometer to measure the concentration of *p*-nitrophenol produced when colorless *p*-nitrophenyl phosphate is hydrolyzed to yellow *p*-nitrophenol.

2. 200- and 1000-μL pipetters from the balance room.

3. 20-μL pipetter: there are two Gilson pipetters in the hood. You will use these pipetters for just a few measurements. You will share these pipetters with the other groups in your laboratory. Do not remove the pipetters from the hood.

4. Extra cardboard box to use as a test tube holder. The boxes are on the reagent bench.

5. Two 100-mL beakers for deionized water and 0.50 M NaOH.

6. Disposable test tubes found on the reagent bench.

Safety

WEAR GLOVES. If you leave the lab, take the gloves off and recycle them so you don't transport any hazardous materials that might be on the gloves outside of the lab. Get new gloves when you return to lab.

Waste Disposal

Have a 600-mL beaker available to collect waste. Put all solutions containing *p*-nitrophenol or *p*-nitrophenyl phosphate into this beaker. At the end of the lab period, pour the waste into the appropriate waste jar. Rinse the beaker with a small amount of water and pour the rinse into the waste jar.

NOTES

Disposable test tubes and vials will be provided for this assay. Please discard all solutions into the appropriate waste jar and dispose of all test tubes and vials in the "glass trash" receptacle. All the reagents in vials must be discarded when you are finished. Leave the cardboard boxes on the reagent bench.

Part I. Prepare a Standard Curve for *p*-Nitrophenol (PN)

Prepare PN Standard Solutions

In question 4 of the Prelab exercises you were asked to calculate the volume of *p*-nitrophenol needed to prepare dilutions of the stock solution. Compare your results to your group members' calculations. Are they the same? If not, figure out who is correct; you will use these answers to prepare dilutions of the stock *p*-nitrophenol that will be used to construct a standard curve.

1. Label seven disposable test tubes 0–6 at the top of the tube so that the labels will not interfere with light passing through the tubes.

2. Use the stock solution of 200 µM *p*-nitrophenol (PN) and pipetters to prepare PN standard solutions as described in question 4, Table 7.1 of the Prelab exercises.

3. Obtain 70 mL of 0.50 M NaOH in a small beaker. Add 1000 µL of 0.50 M sodium hydroxide (NaOH) to each tube. Mix the solutions by holding the tubes near the top and "flicking" the bottom of the tube with your finger to combine the contents.

Sodium hydroxide raises the pH of the solution which increases the light absorption by PN. Notice the more intense yellow color after adding the NaOH.

Measurement of Standard and Assay Solutions with a Genesys Spectrophotometer

©Hayden-McNeil, LLC

Figure 7.4. The Spectronic 20 Genesys™ spectrophotometer.

Using the Spectronic 20 GENESYS™ Spectrophotometer

Initial Preparation

- Make sure the cell holder in the sample compartment is empty before turning on the spectrophotometer.

- Turn the power switch (located at the rear lower left side) to ON ("I").

- Allow the spectrophotometer to warm up for 20 minutes.

Setting the Spectrophotometer to Zero Absorbance with the Blank

- Press the **A/T/C** pad to select the desired mode (A)

- Press the **nm (up)** or **nm (down)** pad to set the wavelength to **405 nm**. (Holding down on the desired key changes the wavelength more quickly.)

- Carefully clean the outside of tube "0," the blank solution, with a Kimwipe. Insert the tube into the cell holder in the sample compartment and close the door.

- Press the **0 ABS/100%T** button to set the absorbance to zero. The spectrophotometer is now zeroed for 405 nm.

Measurement of the Standard and Assay Solutions

- Carefully clean the outside of the tube with a Kimwipe.

- Insert the tube into the cell holder and close the compartment door.

- Record the absorbance of the solutions or assay in your notebook.

- Repeat.

Part II. Measure V_{max} and Determine K_m of Wheat Germ Acid Phosphatase for the Substrate p-Nitrophenyl Phosphate

The following reagents will be used for the assay:

- 10× stock buffer (500 mM sodium acetate, pH 6.0)

- Stock substrate (20 mM p-nitrophenyl phosphate)—keep on ice

- Wheat germ acid phosphatase (0.3 mg/mL)—keep on ice

- 0.5 M NaOH

Like all enzyme-catalyzed reactions, the rate of this reaction is pH dependent. You will therefore be given a 10× buffer solution (500 mM sodium acetate, pH 6.0).

This assay will measure the activity of the phosphatase enzyme over a range of eight different concentrations of substrate (0.10 mM to 12 mM). You will need to prepare eight sets of assay tubes with a range of substrate concentrations spanning 0.10 mM to 12 mM of PNP. Each tube will contain the same concentration of buffer (same pH) and of enzyme and will be run at the same temperature and for the same length of time, 10 minutes. You will initiate each reaction with the addition of 50 µL enzyme and stop the reactions by adding 1000 µL of 0.5 M NaOH.

NOTES

For each concentration of PNP, you will always prepare three assay tubes. Two tubes will have **active** enzyme and the absorbance measurements will be averaged for the **two** identical tubes. The third tube or control will be made inactive by adding the NaOH prior to adding enzyme. The absorbance of this inactive tube will be subtracted from the averaged active results to correct for any absorbance of light not due to activity of the enzyme. See the following schematic.

The best way to set up an assay in which many of the components will be the same is to prepare one mixture of common components that can then be transferred to the three assay tubes. This eliminates a lot of pipetting and ensures that each tube will have the same concentration of components. You will prepare a bit more of this "cocktail" than is needed because some of it will always adhere to the tube in which it is made. The easiest procedure is to make enough cocktail for one extra tube, or 3 + 1 = 4 tubes. Each cocktail will contain the same amount of buffer, but the amount of stock substrate (20 mM PNP) and water will vary. Remember, the 0.5 M NaOH used to stop the reactions is not part of the cocktail. See Table 7.3 and Figure 7.5.

Table 7.3. Contents of the Variable-Substrate Cocktails.

Item	Volume per Assay Tube	Volume per Cocktail
10× Buffer	50 μL	200 μL
Substrate	Variable	Variable
Water	Variable	Variable
Cocktail Total	**450 μL**	**1800 μL**

Enzyme	50 μL	Added to Each Tube
Grand Total	**500 μL**	**2000 μL**

Use the relationship $C_1V_1 = C_2V_2$ to calculate how much (V_1) of the concentrated stock substrate ($C_1 = 20$ mM) to add to each cocktail to obtain the final volume ($V_2 = 2000$ μL) of cocktail at the desired final concentration (C_2). Complete these calculation in Table 7.4 before coming to lab and copy the table into your notebook.

Table 7.4. Calculating Amount of Substrate to Use in Each Cocktail.

Cocktail	C_2, Final Concentration (mM)	V_2, Final Volume (μL)	C_1, Initial Concentration (mM)	V_1, Initial Volume (μL)
A	0.10	2000	20	10
B	0.25	2000	20	
C	0.50	2000	20	
D	1.0	2000	20	
E	2.5	2000	20	
F	5.0	2000	20	
G	10	2000	20	
H	12	2000	20	

In order to keep the final volume of each cocktail the same you will need to add different amounts of water to each cocktail. Complete Table 7.5 **using substrate volumes from Table 7.4**, buffer volumes that are constant (50 µL), and water volumes that you calculate. The first row is completed for you. Note that the total volume of each cocktail is 1800 µL because the enzyme is added later.

Table 7.5. Calculating Volumes of Cocktail Components.

Cocktail	Final PNP Concentration (mM)	Volume of Buffer (µL)	Volume of 20 mM PNP (µL)	Volume of H_2O (µL)	Total Volume of Cocktail without Enzyme (µL)
A	0.10	200	10	1590	1800
B	0.25	200			1800
C	0.50	200	quantities		1800
D	1.0	200	from		1800
E	2.5	200	Table		1800
F	5.0	200	7.4		1800
G	10	200			1800
H	12	200			1800

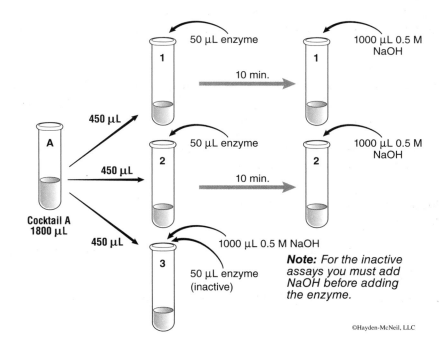

Figure 7.5. Schematic of assay for one concentration of substrate, [PNP] = 0.10 mM.

NOTES

 NOTE: You will be adding a very small amount of PNP to cocktail 1, just 10 μL. Your pipetters will not dispense this volume. There will be two Gilson pipetters available in your laboratory that dispense 10 μL. You must *share* the pipetters with the other groups. Do not remove the pipetters from the hood.

1. Label eight disposable test tubes A–H. Prepare the cocktail mixtures. Mix each solution thoroughly.

For the assay, you will need 24 disposable test tubes. You will prepare three tubes for each concentration of PNP: two tubes will be duplicate assays and the third tube will be inactive. See Figure 7.5 and Table 7.6.

2. Label tubes 1–24 and transfer 450 μL of each cocktail to the appropriate tubes.

To measure the rate of the reaction, it is important to note the time at which the enzyme is added and the time at which the reaction is stopped. Because one cannot possibly add enzyme or stop buffer to all of the tubes simultaneously, you will stagger the addition of enzyme and sodium hydroxide at 30-second intervals. See Table 7.6 for guidance.

As soon as the enzyme and its substrate are mixed, the enzyme will start to generate the product. To stop the reaction after 10 minutes has passed, you will add 1000 μL of 0.5 M NaOH to each tube. The addition of NaOH not only raises the pH to enhance the absorption of light by PN, it also denatures the enzyme, thus stopping the reaction. Adding the NaOH also raises the level of liquid in the tube making spectrophotometric measurements in the assay tubes possible.

3. To each inactive sample, add 1000 μL of 0.5 M NaOH and mix.

4. Start the assay with the addition of 50 μL of enzyme. Immediately mix the contents of the tube by "flicking" the tube with your forefinger. Remember: you will add enzyme to the inactive assays too.

5. After 10 minutes, stop the active assays by adding 1000 μL of 0.5 M NaOH and mix the contents of each tube again.

Measuring Absorbance of Assay Solutions
For each assay:

1. Wipe the outside of the cuvette with a Kimwipe. Insert the tube into the spectrophotometer.

2. Record the absorbance value displayed into your lab notebook.

Table 7.6. Table for Time Tracking and Recording Data for Assay of Acid Phosphatase.

Cocktail	Tube #	[PNP] mM	Start Time (min) Add 50 μL Enzyme	Stop Time (min) Add 1000 μL NaOH	Elapsed Time (min)	ABS	Mean ABS	Corrected ABS
A	1	0.10	0:00	10:00	10:00			
	2	0.10	0:30	10:30	10:00			
	3	0.10	1:00	inactive enzyme				
B	4	0.25	1:30	11:30	10:00			
	5	0.25	2:00	12:00	10:00			
	6	0.25	2:30	inactive enzyme				
C	7	0.50	3:00	13:00	10:00			
	8	0.50	3:30	13:30	10:00			
	9	0.50	4:00	inactive enzyme				
D	10	1.0	4:30	14:30	10:00			
	11	1.0	5:00	15:00	10:00			
	12	1.0	5:30	inactive enzyme				
E	13	2.5	6:00	16:00	10:00			
	14	2.5	6:30	16:30	10:00			
	15	2.5	7:00	inactive enzyme				
F	16	5.0	7:30	17:30	10:00			
	17	5.0	8:00	18:00	10:00			
	18	5.0	8:30	inactive enzyme				
G	19	10	9:00	19:00	10:00			
	20	10	9:30	19:30	10:00			
	21	10	10:00	inactive enzyme				
H	22	12	10:30	20:30	10:00			
	23	12	11:00	21:00	10:00			
	24	12	11:30	inactive enzyme				

Pour contents of all tubes into a beaker. Rinse all the test tubes once and put this rinse into the beaker. Pour contents of the beaker into the designated large waste jar. Rinse your waste beaker once with a small amount of water and put the rinse into the waste container. Dispose of all test tubes and vials in the "glass trash" receptacle.

Part III. Determine the Effect of a Competitive Inhibitor, Inorganic Phosphate (Na$_2$PO$_4$), on the V$_{max}$ and K$_m$ of Acid Phosphatase for *p*-Nitrophenyl Phosphate

To study the effect of inorganic phosphate on the activity of phosphatase, you must prepare solutions of buffered substrate at various concentrations just as you did for Part II except you will add 50 µL of 10 mM sodium phosphate to each tube. You must add 50 µL less water to each tube to keep the total volume of the assay at 500 µL.

Table 7.7. Contents of the Variable-Substrate Cocktails for Inhibition Study.

Item	Volume per Assay Tube	Volume per Cocktail (× 4)
10× Buffer	50 µL	200 µL
Substrate	Variable	Variable
Sodium Phosphate	50 µL	200 µL
Water	Variable	Variable
Cocktail Total	450 µL	1800 µL

Enzyme	50 µL	Added to Each Tube
Grand Total	500 µL	2000 µL

In order to keep the final volume of each cocktail the same you will need to add different amounts of water to each cocktail. Complete Table 7.8 using substrate volumes from Table 7.4, buffer and sodium phosphate volumes that are constant, and water volumes that you calculate. The first row is completed for you. Note that the total volume of each cocktail is 1800 µL because the enzyme is added later.

Table 7.8. Calculating Volumes of Cocktail Components for Inhibition Study.

Cocktail	Final PNP Concentration (mM)	Volume of Buffer (µL)	Volume of 20 mM PNP (µL)	Volume of 10 mM Sodium Phosphate (µL)	Volume of H$_2$O (µL)	Total Volume of Cocktail without Enzyme (µL)
A	0.10	200	10	200	1390	1800
B	0.25	200		200		1800
C	0.50	200	quantities	200		1800
D	1.0	200	from	200		1800
E	2.5	200	Table	200		1800
F	5.0	200	7.4	200		1800
G	10	200		200		1800
H	12	200		200		1800

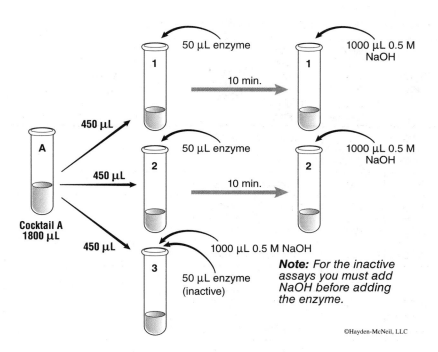

Figure 7.6. Schematic of assay for one concentration of substrate, [PNP] = 0.10 mM.

1. Label disposable test tubes A–H. Prepare cocktails.

2. Label 24 disposable test tubes for the assay. Transfer 450 µL of the cocktail into the appropriate tubes.

3. To each inactive sample add 1000 µL of 0.50 M NaOH.

You should again stagger the times at which you add 50 µL of enzyme to start the reaction and 1000 µL to stop the reaction. Use Table 7.9 for guidance.

4. Start the assay with the addition of 50 µL of enzyme. Immediately mix the contents of the tube by "flicking" the tube with your forefinger. Remember: you will be adding enzyme to the inactive assays too.

5. After 10 minutes, stop the active assays by adding 1000 µL of 0.5 M NaOH and mix the contents of each tube again.

6. Measure the absorbance of each assay and record in your notebook.

Table 7.9. Table for Time Tracking and Recording Data for Assay of Acid Phosphatase.

Cocktail	Tube #	[PNP] mM	Start Time (min) Add 50 µL Enzyme	Stop Time (min) Add 1000 µL NaOH	Elapsed Time (min)	ABS	Mean ABS	Corrected ABS
A	1	0.10	0:00	10:00	10:00			
	2	0.10	0:30	10:30	10:00			
	3	0.10	1:00	inactive enzyme				
B	4	0.25	1:30	11:30	10:00			
	5	0.25	2:00	12:00	10:00			
	6	0.25	2:30	inactive enzyme				
C	7	0.50	3:00	13:00	10:00			
	8	0.50	3:30	13:30	10:00			
	9	0.50	4:00	inactive enzyme				
D	10	1.0	4:30	14:30	10:00			
	11	1.0	5:00	15:00	10:00			
	12	1.0	5:30	inactive enzyme				
E	13	2.5	6:00	16:00	10:00			
	14	2.5	6:30	16:30	10:00			
	15	2.5	7:00	inactive enzyme				
F	16	5.0	7:30	17:30	10:00			
	17	5.0	8:00	18:00	10:00			
	18	5.0	8:30	inactive enzyme				
G	19	10	9:00	19:00	10:00			
	20	10	9:30	19:30	10:00			
	21	10	10:00	inactive enzyme				
H	22	12	10:30	20:30	10:00			
	23	12	11:00	21:00	10:00			
	24	12	11:30	inactive enzyme				

Waste Disposal and Cleanup

Dispose of all solutions containing *p*-nitrophenol and *p*-nitrophenyl phosphate into your waste beaker. Rinse all reaction tubes and vials **once** and add to waste beaker. Put all the waste from your waste beaker into the waste jar. Rinse your waste beaker once with a small amount of water and put the rinse into the waste container.

Turn off the Spec Genesys and return it to the back of the room.

Return pipetters to cabinet in the balance room.

Dispose of all test tubes and vials in the "glass trash" receptacle. Keep your splash goggles on until you have cleaned up your work area and are leaving the lab. Lock your lab drawer before leaving lab. Leave the cardboard boxes on the reagent bench.

Postlab

Part I. Prepare a Standard Curve for *p*-Nitrophenol

Prepare a standard curve by plotting absorbance vs. concentration of *p*-nitrophenol standards (in M). Include the blank as the 0,0 point in your graph. Display the equation of the trendline or best-fit line and the R^2 value on the graph. Calculate the molar absorptivity of *p*-nitrophenol using the trendline. Attach a copy of the standard curve to your report.

Part II. Measure V_{max} and Determine K_m of Wheat Germ Acid Phosphatase for the Substrate *p*-Nitrophenyl Phosphate

Average the absorbance values of the two active tubes for each concentration of substrate. Subtract the absorbance value of the inactive tube to find the corrected absorbance. Use the molar absorptivity you found in Part I to calculate the concentration of *p*-nitrophenol from the corrected absorbance values. Calculate the specific activity (V) in μmoles/min/mg of protein for each concentration of substrate (see Prelab question 6). You can construct a formula in Excel to do the calculations.

Generate two separate graphs: 1) Michaelis-Menten plot (V vs. [S]), and 2) Lineweaver-Burk plot (1/V vs. 1/[S]). Label each axis and be sure to indicate the appropriate units on each axis (e.g., [S] is measured in mM). In the Lineweaver-Burk plot, fit a trendline to your data. Estimate V_{max} and K_m (including appropriate units) from the Michaelis-Menten plot. Calculate the values of V_{max} and K_m (including appropriate units) using the trendline from the Lineweaver-Burk plot. Show your work for all calculations.

NOTES

Part III. Determine the Effect of a Competitive Inhibitor, Inorganic Phosphate (Na_2PO_4), on the V_{max} and K_m of Acid Phosphatase for _p_-nitrophenyl Phosphate

Follow the same data analysis outlined previously to generate a Lineweaver-Burk plot using the data from the enzyme with the inhibitor. Calculate the values of V_{max} and K_m (including appropriate units) using the trendline from the plot.

Postlab Questions

1. Compare your calculated values of V_{max} and K_m for the enzyme with and without an inhibitor. How does the presence of the inhibitor affect V_{max} and K_m?

2. Predict what would happen to the values of V_{max} and K_m (increase, decrease, or stay the same) if the same inhibitor were used at a higher concentration. Justify your answer based on your data.

3. How does the inhibitor, inorganic phosphate, interact with the enzyme, acid phosphatase? Explain in words and draw a picture to show this and label the enzyme, substrate, and inhibitor.

CHAPTER 8

Iron(III) Thiocyanate Equilibrium System and Le Châtelier's Principle

Introduction

In this lab you will study four systems that will help you to understand chemical equilibrium and Le Châtelier's principle.

Iron(III) Thiocyanate Equilibrium System

In this lab you will observe the differences in color intensity in several equilibrium mixtures and obtain a quantitative measure of the concentration of the colored species $FeSCN^{2+}(aq)$ in the following equilibrium system.

$$Fe^{3+}(aq) + SCN^-(aq) \rightleftharpoons FeSCN^{2+}(aq) \quad K_{eq} = ? \qquad (1)$$

$$\text{(pale yellow) (colorless)} \quad \text{(orange-red)}$$

You will determine the concentration of $FeSCN^{2+}(aq)$ in these equilibrium mixtures by comparing absorbance values with a $FeSCN^{2+}$ standard curve. You will then calculate the concentration of $Fe^{3+}(aq)$ and $SCN^-(aq)$ in the equilibrium mixtures and ultimately calculate an experimental value of the equilibrium constant, K, for the equilibrium system.

The amount of light of a particular wavelength absorbed by a substance dissolved in water depends on the concentration of the absorbing species, the molar absorptivity for the substance at the particular wavelength, and the length of light path through the solution. This relationship is known as the Beer-Lambert law.

absorbance = (molar absorptivity) × (path length) × (concentration)   (2)

$$A = \varepsilon \ell C$$

You will use a spectrophotometer to measure the absorbance of your $FeSCN^{2+}$ standards at a particular wavelength. When you graph absorbance (y) vs. concentration (x), the slope of the trendline or best-fit line corresponds to the molar absorptivity of $FeSCN^{2+}$ at that wavelength. (The path length in this experiment is 1 cm.) You can then use Equation 2 to calculate the concentrations of $FeSCN^{2+}$

in your equilibrium mixtures using the experimental absorbance values. Refer to the spectrophotometry information provided in How to Be Successful in CHM 12901: A Guide to Using Laboratory Equipment and Instrumentation at the beginning of this manual.

Calculating Equilibrium Concentrations

The equilibrium concentrations of Fe^{3+} and SCN^- are calculated using an ICE table. The acronym ICE refers to the three concentrations that are calculated with the table: Initial concentration, Change in concentration and Equilibrium concentration. An example of using an ICE table to solve equilibrium problems follows.

Calcium ions (Ca^{2+}) react with pyrophosphate ($P_2O_7^{4-}$) to form a complex in aqueous solution according to the reaction below:

$$Ca^{2+}(aq) + P_2O_7^{4-}(aq) \longleftrightarrow CaP_2(aq)$$

In a solution, the initial concentration of Ca^{2+} is 0.002 M and the initial concentration of $P_2O_7^{4-}$ is 0.003 M. At equilibrium, the concentration of $CaP_2O_7^{2-}$ is 0.0019 M. Calculate the value of the equilibrium constant, K, for this reaction.

Step 1: Write equilibrium constant expression, K, in terms of the product and reactant concentrations from the balanced equation for the reaction.

$$K = \frac{[CaP_2O_7^{2-}]}{[Ca^{2+}][P_2O_7^{4-}]}$$

Step 2: Construct an ICE table using the information given in the problem. **I** stands for initial concentration, **C** stands for the change in concentration, and **E** stands for the equilibrium concentration of all products and reactants.

	Ca^{2+}	$P_2O_7^{4-}$	$CaP_2O_7^{2-}$
I	0.002 M	0.003 M	0 M
C	−x	−x	+x
E	0.002 M − x	0.003 M − x	x

Step 3: Since we know the concentration of $CaP_2O_7^{2-}$ at equilibrium, we can fill that in as well, which in this case is equal to x, the change in concentration. Using that information, we can solve for the equilibrium concentrations of Ca^{2+} and $P_2O_7^{2-}$.

	Ca^{2+}	$P_2O_7^{4-}$	$CaP_2O_7^{2-}$
I	0.002 M	0.003 M	0 M
C	−x	−x	+x
E	0.002 M − x	0.003 M − x	x = 0.0019 M

$[Ca^{2+}] = 0.002\ M - 0.0019\ M = 0.0001\ M$

$[P_2O_7^{4-}] = 0.003\ M - 0.0019\ M = 0.0011\ M$

	Ca^{2+}	$P_2O_7^{4-}$	$CaP_2O_7^{2-}$
I	0.002 M	0.003 M	0 M
C	−0.0019 M	−0.0019 M	+0.0019 M
E	0.0001 M	0.0011 M	0.0019 M

Step 4: Once we have found all of the concentrations at equilibrium, we can plug them into the equilibrium constant expression we wrote earlier to find the value of K. Remember that K does not have units.

$$K = \frac{0.0019}{(0.0001)(0.0011)}$$
$$K = 17272$$

Le Châtelier's Principle

Understanding how chemical systems behave requires some knowledge about chemical equilibrium. An important concept in chemical equilibrium focuses on understanding the effects of stressing chemical equilibrium systems. Your textbook contains a great deal of information about chemical equilibrium systems and you should use your textbook as a reference, introduction, and source of background information for this project.

The goals of this project are for you to:

- Investigate what effects might result from adding various substances to equilibrium mixtures.

- Describe the chemistry taking place when the amount of any substance changes in an equilibrium mixture.

- Identify any patterns in the use of particular substances that bring about changes in equilibrium mixtures.

- Explain the effect of heating or cooling an equilibrium mixture.

- Communicate your findings in a lab report.

Background Information

In this lab you will prepare a saturated solution of sodium chloride. A saturated solution is one in which the maximum amount of solute is dissolved in the solution at a certain temperature. The dissolved solute and the undissolved solute are in equilibrium in the saturated solution. If you add more solute to the saturated solution, it will not dissolve. Your textbook contains more information about solubility as an equilibrium process.

An indicator is a substance whose solution changes color due to changes in pH (i.e., H_3O^+ concentration). In this experiment you will use the bromophenol blue indicator to monitor the equilibrium of acetic acid, CH_3COOH, and its conjugate base, CH_3COO^-. The bromophenol blue indicator is yellow in acidic solution (HBrm) and indigo in basic solution (Brm^-). See Figure 8.1.

NOTES

NOTES

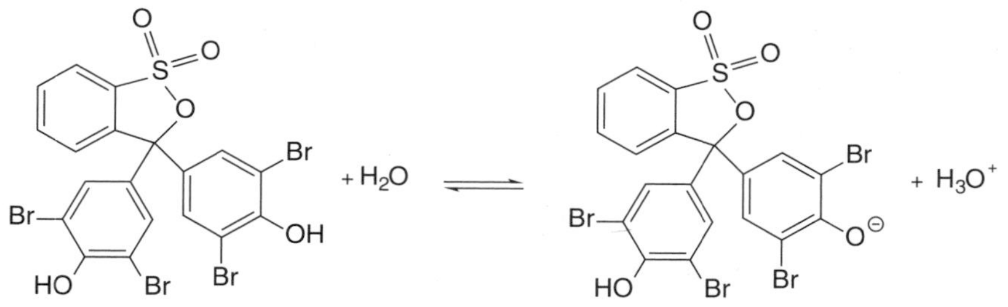

$$HBrm + H_2O \rightleftharpoons Brm^- + H_3O^+$$

Figure 8.1. Protonation and deprotonation of HBrm.

Prelab

As part of your individual preparation for lab, read the experiment and answer the following questions in your lab notebook before going to lab. The copy of your answers on perforated pages from your lab notebook is due at the beginning of lab.

1. Write the equilibrium expression, K, for the iron thiocyanate equilibrium system being used in this lab activity.

2. The wavelength of light used in spectrophotometric measurements is crucial to obtaining good results; however, the wavelength is not used in the calculations. Why is the wavelength selection so important?

3. Calculate the concentrations of each of the standard solutions that you will prepare using the information on pages 117–119 and in Table 8.3.

Table 8.1. Concentration of Standard Solutions of $FeSCN^{2+}$.

Standard	Volume of 0.200 M $Fe(NO_3)_3$ (mL)	Volume of 0.00200 M KSCN (mL)	Total Volume (mL)	$[FeSCN^{2+}]$ (M)
1	10.00	1.50		
2	10.00	2.00		
3	10.00	2.50		
4	10.00	3.00		

4. Calculate the initial concentrations of Fe^{3+} and SCN^- in each of the equilibrium mixtures that you will prepare.

Table 8.2. Initial Concentration of Fe^{3+} and SCN^- in the Equilibrium Mixtures.

Mixture	Volume of 0.00200 M $Fe(NO_3)_3$ (mL)	Volume of 0.00200 M KSCN (mL)	Total Volume (mL)	Initial $[Fe^{3+}]$ (M)	Initial $[SCN^-]$ (M)
A	2.00	8.00	10.00		
B	2.50	7.50	10.00		
C	5.00	5.00	10.00		
D	7.50	2.50	10.00		
E	8.00	2.00	10.00		

5. Given that an aqueous solution of $Co(H_2O)_6{}^{2+}$ is pink and an aqueous solution of $Co(NH_3)_6{}^{2+}$ is blue, answer the following questions about an equilibrium system involving these cobalt(II) ions.

$$Co(H_2O)_6{}^{2+}(aq) + 6\ NH_3(aq) \rightleftharpoons Co(NH_3)_6{}^{2+}(aq) + 2\ H_2O(\ell)$$

Assume that you have a solution containing $Co(H_2O)_6{}^{2+}(aq)$.

a. Predict what you should observe when $NH_3(aq)$ is added to the solution.

b. Explain why you made the prediction using concepts from Le Châtelier's principle.

c. Write the chemical formula of the substance that increased in amount as a result of adding $NH_3(aq)$ to the $Co(H_2O)_6{}^{2+}$ solution. Write the formula of the substance that decreased in amount.

6. In your laboratory notebook, record the experimental procedure you will follow in lab. The procedure is your experimental plan and can be organized as an outline, a flowchart, or a numbered list of steps. You should also include a statement of the purpose of the experiment, notes on safety, and a reference to the relevant pages in your laboratory manual. The copy of your procedure on the duplicate pages of your lab notebook is due at the beginning of lab.

NOTES

FeSCN²⁺ Equilibrium System Flowchart

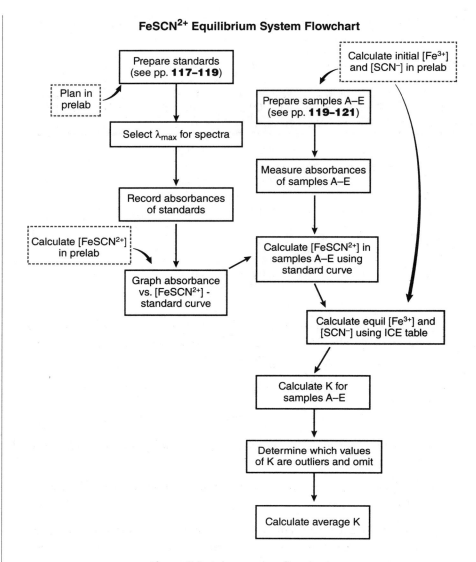

Figure 8.2. Lab procedure flowchart.

Experimental Design

Iron(III) Thiocyanate

The following solutions will be provided in lab:

NOTES

0.200 M $Fe(NO_3)_3$—75 mL per group

0.00200 M KSCN—75 mL per group

You will perform the following steps and calculations in lab:

- Prepare $FeSCN^{2+}$ standard solutions.
- Measure the absorbances of the $FeSCN^{2+}$ standards and use the data to generate a standard curve.
- Prepare 100 mL of 0.00200 M $Fe(NO_3)_3$.
- Prepare five equilibrium mixtures containing various concentrations of $FeSCN^{2+}$.
- Select the appropriate wavelength setting for your absorbance measurements.
- Measure the absorbances of the equilibrium mixtures and determine the $[FeSCN^{2+}]$ in each mixture using your standard curve.
- Calculate the initial *and* equilibrium concentrations of Fe^{3+} and SCN^- in the equilibrium mixtures. You should have calculated the initial concentration in Prelab question 4.
- Calculate an experimental equilibrium constant, K, for each of the equilibrium mixtures.

Important notes about the process:

- Clean all the glassware before you begin working. Adequate rinsing with deionized water is required since our tap water contains iron.
- Adequate mixing of all solutions is very important.
- You will need to keep track of the many solutions used in this lab so proper labeling of test tubes and solutions will be necessary. You might find a black Sharpie (permanent ink) to be very useful.

Data Collection

Lab work is done in groups. Each person must record a complete set of data for standards in his/her lab notebook and turn in the duplicate copy on the perforated pages from the lab notebook at the end of lab.

Prepare Standard Solutions of $FeSCN^{2+}$

Standard solutions must be prepared quantitatively and carefully so that the concentrations can be calculated precisely and accurately. This means that you want to use volumes of solutions that are measured precisely and accurately

NOTES

with volumetric glassware, such as burets or pipets. See the section Volumetric Measurement Techniques in How to Be Successful in CHM 12901: A Guide to Using Laboratory Equipment and Instrumentation at the beginning of this manual for detailed information.

Your group will prepare four standard solutions. The standards will be prepared in 25.00-mL volumetric flasks using **0.200 M Fe(NO$_3$)$_3$** and 0.00200 M KSCN solutions. The volume of each solution in each standard is indicated in Table 8.3. Note: a large excess of Fe^{3+} ion will be used to prepare the standard solutions. This will drive the reaction to completion. Under these circumstances you will be able to calculate the FeSCN^{2+} concentration assuming that the SCN$^-$ is the limiting reagent.

Table 8.3. Preparation of Standard Solutions of FeSCN^{2+}.

Standard	Volume of 0.200 M Fe(NO$_3$)$_3$ (mL)	Volume of 0.00200 M KSCN (mL)
1	10.00	1.50
2	10.00	2.00
3	10.00	2.50
4	10.00	3.00

Set up two 50-mL burets to measure the volumes of 0.200 M Fe(NO$_3$)$_3$ and 0.00200 M KSCN.

Dispense the amounts shown in Table 8.3 directly from the buret into the 25.00 mL volumetric flasks.

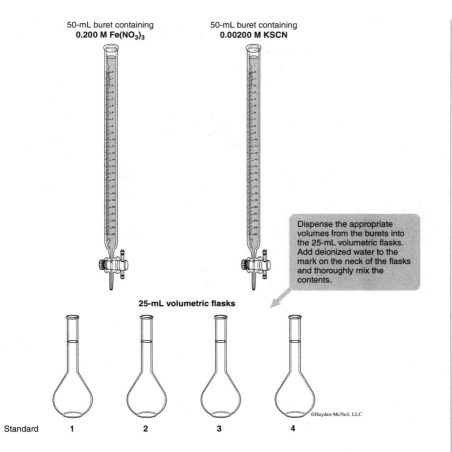

Figure 8.3. Dispense iron(III) nitrate and potassium nitrate directly into 25-mL flasks.

Dilute each standard solution to 25.00 mL by adding deionized water to the volumetric flask to the calibration mark. Use an eyedropper to add the final drops of deionized water. Cover the flask with a small piece of Parafilm and invert several times to mix thoroughly.

Create a table in your lab notebook to record each standard's concentration and absorbance.

Equilibrium Mixtures Containing FeSCN^{2+}

Your group will prepare five equilibrium mixtures with varying amounts of iron(III) nitrate and potassium thiocyanate. For the preparation of the equilibrium mixtures you will need 0.00200 M Fe(NO$_3$)$_3$. You will prepare this solution by carefully diluting the 0.200 M Fe(NO$_3$)$_3$. See Figure 8.4.

NOTES

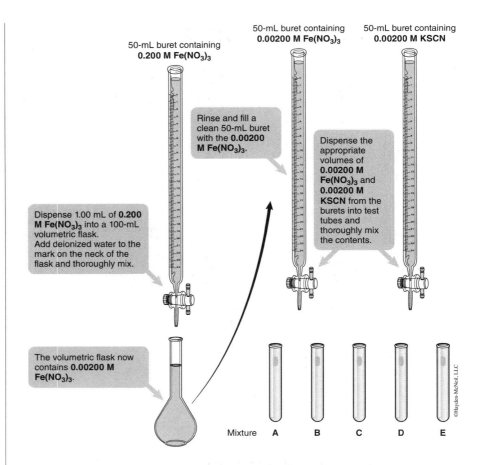

Figure 8.4. Preparing equilibrium mixtures.

- Use the 50-mL buret to add 1.00 mL of 0.200 M $Fe(NO_3)_3$ to a 100.0-mL volumetric flask.

- Add deionized water to the mark on the flask, cover with a small piece of Parafilm, and invert several times to thoroughly mix the contents.

- Rinse and fill a 50-mL buret with the 0.00200 M $Fe(NO_3)_3$.

Now that you have prepared the diluted iron(III) nitrate solution, proceed to prepare the five $FeSCN^{2+}$ equilibrium mixtures using the information in Table 8.4, Figure 8.4, and the following procedure:

- The equilibrium mixtures will be prepared in medium-sized test tubes. Label the test tubes A–E.

- **0.00200 M $Fe(NO_3)_3$** and 0.00200 M KSCN will be used to prepare the equilibrium mixtures.

- Dispense the appropriate volumes of 0.00200 M $Fe(NO_3)_3$ and 0.00200 M KSCN by buret directly into the test tubes. See Table 8.4.

- Cover tubes with a piece of Parafilm and invert to mix.

Table 8.4. Preparation of FeSCN^{2+} Equilibrium Mixtures.

Mixture	Volume of 0.00200 M Fe(NO$_3$)$_3$ (mL)	Volume of 0.00200 M KSCN (mL)	Total Volume (mL)
A	2.00	8.00	10.00
B	2.50	7.50	10.00
C	5.00	5.00	10.00
D	7.50	2.50	10.00
E	8.00	2.00	10.00

Create a table in your lab notebook to record the exact volumes of all reagents used to prepare your equilibrium mixtures and the absorbance of each equilibrium mixture.

Connect the Spectrophotometer to the LabQuest 2
! THE FOLLOWING STEPS MUST BE PERFORMED IN ORDER.

USB-A connect to LabQuest

USB-B connect to SpectroVis

1. Insert the USB-A into the LabQuest.

2. Attach the power adapter to the LabQuest and plug it in.

3. Turn on the LabQuest and wait for the **Meter** screen to appear.

4. Connect the USB-B end of the cable to the SpectroVis.

5. The LabQuest screen will display **USB: Abs**.

Set the Vernier SpectroVis Plus to Zero Absorbance

1. From the **Sensors** menu, choose **Calibrate > USB: Spectrometer**. The calibration dialog box will display the message: "Taking dark sample" then "Waiting 90 seconds for lamp to warm up."

2. When warmup is complete, rinse and fill a cuvette at least ¾ full with deionized water (blank solution).

3. Wipe the outside of the cuvette with a Kimwipe and insert it into the spectrophotometer.

4. Click **Finish Calibration,** then **OK**.

5. Discard the blank solution.

NOTES

Set the Wavelength of the Spectrophotometer

1. Rinse the cuvette with a small amount of Standard Solution #3. Discard the rinse. Fill the cuvette about ¾ full with Standard Solution #3. Wipe the outside of the cuvette with a Kimwipe and insert it into the spectrometer.

2. Tap on the **green arrow** to start data collection. You will see a graph of the spectrum for $FeSCN^{2+}$.

3. Tap on the **red square** to stop data collection.

4. Move the cursor along the graph to choose the maximum absorbance. The wavelength and absorbance will be displayed to the right of the graph. Record the maximum wavelength, concentration, and absorbance of Standard Solution #3 in your notebook.

5. Now set the collection mode, by tapping the meter icon, .

6. Tap on the grey **Mode** box. Tap on **Mode** and choose **Time Based**.

7. Click **OK** and **Discard** the spectrum data.

Measurement of the Standard FeSCN²⁺ Solutions

Now that the parameters are set for the LabQuest and spectrometer, all you need to do to measure absorbance of a sample is to insert the sample into the spectrometer.

You should have recorded the absorbance of Standard Solution #3 and can now continue with the remaining standard solutions from the least concentrated (1) to the most concentrated (4) and your equilibrium mixtures:

1. Discard the solution in the cuvette, if you haven't already done so.

2. Rinse and fill the cuvette about ¾ full with the next standard solution. Wipe the outside of the cuvette with a Kimwipe and insert it into the spectrophotometer.

3. Wait a few seconds and record the absorbance displayed and concentration of the solution in your lab notebook.

4. Repeat with the other standard solutions.

Measurement of the Equilibrium Mixtures

1. Discard the standard solution in the cuvette.

2. Rinse and fill the cuvette with the Equilibrium Mixture to be measured. Wipe the outside of the cuvette with a Kimwipe and insert it into the spectrometer.

3. Wait a few seconds and record the absorbance displayed in your lab notebook.

4. Repeat with the remaining mixtures.

Transfer the Data to an Excel File

Open Excel. Enter your data (concentration and absorbance) from the measurement of the standard solutions of $FeSCN^{2+}$. Save the data.

Data Analysis

$FeSCN^{2+}$ Standard Curve

Prepare a standard curve for $FeSCN^{2+}$ (Absorbance versus Concentration of $FeSCN^{2+}$). Display the trendline and R-squared value on the graph. Print your standard curve for inclusion with your report. Make sure the title and axes are labeled, and the equation for the best linear fit is shown.

Equilibrium Mixtures

Calculation of Fe^{2+}, SCN^- and $FeSCN^{2+}$ can be done using a spreadsheet program such as Excel. In the report you must show the equations used and your full work for one of the mixtures.

1. Calculate the concentration of $FeSCN^{2+}$ in each mixture using the absorbance (measured in lab) and the trend line from your standard curve.

2. Knowing the initial concentration of Fe^{3+} and SCN^- (calculated in the prelab) as well as the equilibrium concentration of $FeSCN^{2+}$ in each mixture (calculated in question 1), calculate the equilibrium concentrations of Fe^{3+} and SCN^- using the equilibrium table method (ICE table) presented in your textbook and in lecture.

3. Using the equilibrium concentrations of each of the three species in the equilibrium system, calculate a value for the equilibrium constant, K, for each mixture.

4. Calculate an average value of K. First, decide if any of the experimentally determined K values should be omitted from the average value calculation.

Le Châtelier's Principle

You and your group will design procedures to determine whether various substances act as a stress on equilibrium mixtures.

Use samples of ~5 mL of the equilibrium mixtures for testing. Your design must keep reagent use to a minimum so you will need to add solutions in a drop-by-drop fashion and add only a few crystals of solids at a time.

NOTES

Keep complete records of what you did as well as what changes you observed so that you could repeat the process exactly if needed.

Lab work is done in groups.

Each person must record a complete set of data in his/her lab notebook and turn in the duplicate copy of these data on the perforated pages from the lab notebook at the end of lab.

! **Watch out—You can easily contaminate the reagents. Do not touch droppers to sides of test tubes. Do not dispense the solids with the same spatula or wooden splint.**

Equilibrium System 1

Equation

$$Fe^{3+}(aq) + SCN^-(aq) \rightleftharpoons FeSCN^{2+}(aq)$$

(yellow)   (colorless)   (orange/red)

Preparation
Put 8 drops of 1 M $Fe(NO_3)_3$ and 8 drops of 1 M NH_4SCN into 100 mL of deionized water. This solution will be your initial equilibrium mixture as well as your standard for color comparisons of all other mixtures. Use about 5 mL of this solution for each test.

Test Reagents or Conditions
cooling/ice bath

heating/boiling water bath

KSCN(s)

0.25 M NH_3

$Fe(NO_3)_3$(s)

0.1 M $AgNO_3$ (special waste disposal)

0.25 M NaOH

0.25 M Na_2HPO_4

Design procedures to test if reagents or conditions bring about a shift in equilibrium position when added to the equilibrium system.

Notes
Each test procedure should begin with about 5 mL of the equilibrium mixture. Use test reagent dropwise or very few solid crystals per test. In most of your tests, equilibrium shifts will be apparent upon the addition of 3 drops of solution or a few crystals.

Perform each test reaction one (1) time per group.

WEAR GLOVES. If you leave the lab, take the gloves off and recycle them so you don't transport any hazardous materials that might be on the gloves outside of the lab. Get new gloves when you return to lab.

Waste Disposal

! Any mixture containing Ag^+ must be put into the identified waste disposal container. All other solutions and mixtures can be poured down the drain followed by lots of water.

Rinse all glassware at least three times with deionized water.

Analysis

Write a chemical equation that represents the equilibrium system.

For each change observed:

*   Identify the direction of the equilibrium shift.
*   Identify the change in the amount of $FeSCN^{2+}$ compared to the standard.

What conclusion(s) can you make about the exo- or endothermicity of the reaction based on your observations of the system in the ice and warm water baths?

Equilibrium System 2: Saturated NaCl Solution

Equation

$$NaCl(s) \rightleftharpoons Na^+(aq) + Cl^-(aq)$$

Preparation

To prepare a saturated solution of NaCl, first place about 4 spatulafuls of solid NaCl into a medium-sized test tube. Fill the tube about 1/2 full with deionized water. Cover and seal the test tube with Parafilm and shake it to dissolve the NaCl. If, after shaking, all the solid dissolves, add more NaCl until excess solid remains in the bottom of the tube. Into a clean, dry, small test tube, carefully decant (decant means to pour off the liquid without transfering solid) a portion of the saturated solution so that the test tube is about half full.

Test Reagent

You will use concentrated HCl (12 M) as the test reagent.

! WEAR GLOVES and handle 12 M HCl very carefully because it is corrosive and can cause eye and skin burns. Keep the reagent bottle in the main hood—inhalation may cause severe irritation of the respiratory tract.

To the small test tube, add concentrated HCl (12 M) dropwise until you see a distinct change. Record your observations in your laboratory notebook. To the same solution, add DI water until you see a distinct change again. Record your observations.

Analysis

When you added concentrated HCl and then water to the saturated NaCl solution, were your observations consistent with Le Châtelier's principle? Comment on any equilibrium shifts that occurred.

Equilibrium System 3: Acetic Acid Solution

Test the Indicator

You will add acid or base to a small amount of indicator in water to observe the indicator's color change in response to a change in H_3O^+ concentration. Label two medium-sized test tubes "acidic" and "basic." To the appropriate tube, add the following:

Put 2 drops of bromophenol blue into 5 mL of water and add a few drops of 6 M HCl. Record the color.

Put 2 drops of bromophenol blue into 5 mL of water and add a few drops of 6 M NaOH. Record the color.

Equation

$$CH_3COOH + H_2O \rightleftharpoons CH_3COO^- + H_3O^+$$

Preparation

Put about 5 mL of 0.10 M acetic acid solution in a medium-sized test tube and add 2 drops of bromophenol blue indicator. Record the color. Retain this solution as a reference.

Test Reagents

$CH_3COONa(s)$

0.25 M NaOH

Test each reagent above to see if it brings about a shift in equilibrium position (that is, a change in H_3O^+ concentration) when added to acetic acid. Begin each test with 5 mL of 0.10 M acetic acid and add 2 drops of bromophenol blue to detect any shift in equilibrium.

For CH_3COONa, add a few crystals of test reagent to a 5-mL sample of the acetic acid solution with bromophenol blue added. Record your observations.

For 0.25 M NaOH, first add 3 drops, slowly and with stirring, to a 5-mL sample of the acetic acid solution with bromophenol blue added. Record your observations after each drop. Next add more 3 drops of NaOH solution to the same test tube, slowly and with stirring. Record your observations.

Analysis

In each of your tests of the acetic acid equilibrium, identify the overall change in amount of H_3O^+ as compared to the original acetic acid solution.

Answer the following questions based on the individual tests:

1. **Test Reagent:** CH_3COONa

   a. Write the equilibrium equation for the dissociation of CH_3COONa in water.

   b. What is the initial effect on the acetic acid equilibrium when CH_3COONa is added?

   c. According to Le Châtelier's principle, how does the acetic acid dissociation equilibrium shift in response to the addition of CH_3COONa? What is the overall change in $[H_3O^+]$ in the solution? (Consider the color change of the indicator.) How would one explain this change based on the shift of equilibria?

2. **Test Reagent:** NaOH

   a. Write the equation(s) for the reaction(s) that occur(s) when NaOH is added to the acetic acid solution.

   b. How does the addition of 3 drops of NaOH solution initially affect the amount of H_3O^+ in the acetic acid solution? (Explain based on the color(s) you observed.) Using Le Châtelier's principle, explain how the acetic acid dissociation equilibrium shifts in response to this change (3 drops of NaOH solution).

   c. How did the addition of 6 drops of NaOH solution affect the overall amount of H_3O^+ as compared to the initial acetic acid solution? *(Use your color observations as part of your explanation.)* According to Le Châtelier's principle, in which direction would you expect the acetic acid equilibrium to shift after the addition of 6 drops of NaOH solution? Were your color observations consistent with your prediction? Why or why not?

Record your observations.

Cleanup

All the solutions—with the exception of solutions containing silver—can be discarded down the drain followed by large amounts of water.

Cuvettes can be discarded in the trash.

All glassware must be rinsed at least three times with water (once with tap water followed by two rinses with deionized water).

NOTES

Return the 25-mL burets and volumetric flask to your instructor. Return all other equipment to its proper place.

Disconnect the LabQuest, DC Adapter, USB connector, and spectrophotometer to the box on your bench.

Keep your splash goggles on until you have completed the data analysis, turned in your report, and are leaving the lab. Lock your lab drawer before leaving lab.

Waste Disposal

Dispose of solutions containing silver in the waste jar provided. All other solutions can be poured down the drain followed by lots of water.

Rinse all glassware at least three times with deionized water.

Analysis

For each change observed, explain the change in terms of the increase or decrease in the amount of H_3O^+. Indicate the direction of the equilibrium shift.

The Laboratory Report

Your group is to prepare one lab report following the guidelines and outline described on pages x–xii.

Remember, it is your responsibility as a group to ensure that everyone whose name is on the report participated as fully as possible in the project.

The due date and time will be communicated to you by your instructor. Reports will usually be due at the beginning of lab the week after the experiment was completed.

Lab Notebook Pages

Before you leave lab, turn in the duplicate pages from your lab notebook where you recorded data and observations as you completed the lab work.

CHAPTER 9

Acid–Base Equilibria: Monoprotic Acids

The goal of this experiment is to determine the concentration of a strong base and a weak acid using two types of acid–base titration techniques. One type of titration will allow you to experimentally determine the equilibrium constant for a weak acid. You will also compare the accuracy of each titration method as well as the difference between a strong acid–strong base and a weak acid–strong base titration.

Introduction: Acid–Base Titrations

Reactions between acids and bases that are dissolved in water occur almost instantaneously; they occur as fast as the two solutions can be mixed. These reactions also tend to go to completion, reacting until all of the limiting reagent is consumed. When exact stoichiometric amounts of acid and base have been mixed, the reaction is said to have reached the **equivalence point**. Essentially all of the acid has reacted with the base, and vice versa.

The technique of slowly adding an acid to a base—or vice versa—until the reaction has reached the equivalence point is known as a **titration**. In this lab, you will perform two types of acid–base titrations: colorimetric titrations and pH (or potentiometric) titrations.

Colorimetric Titrations

One way to determine the equivalence point of a titration is the use of an **indicator** to show when the equivalence point of the reaction has been reached. Indicators take many forms, but often are substances whose solutions change color due to changes in pH. The most familiar indicators are litmus and phenolphthalein. Phenolphthalein is colorless in acid and pink in base.

In theory, the indicator should turn color at the equivalence point. In practice, each indicator has an **endpoint**—the pH at which it turns color—that might be slightly different from the pH for the equivalence point of the reaction. Titrations of a strong acid with a strong base that use phenolphthalein as the indicator,

NOTES

for example, should be stopped *just before* the solution turns a permanent pink color. In this fashion, the endpoint of the indicator (pH 8.3) is brought as closely as possible to the equivalence point of the reaction (pH 7 for strong acid–strong base titration).

In this lab, your first colorimetric titration will be a "**scout**" **titration**, in which you will add the titrant continuously at a moderate rate to find the approximate volume at the equivalence point. This "scout volume" provides an estimate which allows you to conduct subsequent titrations with better accuracy. The second colorimetric titration will be done more carefully and slowly to find a more **accurate** measurement of the volume at the equivalence point.

pH (Potentiometric) Titrations

In a potentiometric (pH) titration, the equivalence point is determined using a pH titration curve, which is a plot of pH (y-axis) vs. volume of titrant added (x-axis). In this lab, you will use the Logger *Pro* program to record and plot the data. Indicators are not used in potentiometric titrations since they have acid–base characteristics.

Figure 9.1 shows a pH titration curve for the titration of acetic acid with NaOH. The sharp rise in pH indicates the equivalence point, the point at which all of the acetic acid has reacted with the NaOH that has been added.

Finding the Equivalence Point: Three Methods

To find the volume of titrant at the equivalence point using a pH titration curve, use the following steps:

Method 1 (Schematic)

1. Draw a line that follows the linear portion of the curve *before* the equivalence point.

2. Draw a line that follows the linear portion of the curve *after* the equivalence point.

3. Draw a line that follows the most linear portion of the steep vertical part of the curve. Points A and B are the points where this line intersects the 2 previously drawn lines.

4. Determine the midpoint between points A and B; this is the equivalence point.

5. Draw a perpendicular line from the equivalence point to the x-axis. This volume is the volume required to reach the equivalence point of the titration.

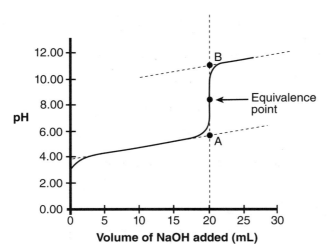

Figure 9.1. Titration curve and volume at the equivalence point.

Methods 2 and 3 (Mathematical)

Another more accurate method to determine the equivalence point is by using the 1st or 2nd derivative of the pH titration curve data. The Logger *Pro* program used in this experiment allows you to view and save the 1st and 2nd derivative data. Using the 1st derivative data, the equivalence point is the plot maximum. Using the 2nd derivative data, the equivalence point is the point where the curve crosses zero on the x-axis between the curve's maximum and minimum y-value.

To find the equivalence point using the derivative method, it is necessary to focus in on a smaller range of values on the x-axis. You can expand the x-axis within a small range before and after the equivalence point and find the volume of NaOH added to within two places beyond the decimal. The best range to view the curve is within ±0.50 mL of the equivalence point. This is a very simple operation in the Logger *Pro* program. See instructions later in this chapter.

For the 1st derivative method, find the x-value (mL NaOH) where the curve reaches its maximum.

For the 2nd derivative method, the equivalence point is the value (mL NaOH) where the curve crosses zero between the maximum and minimum y-value.

A pH titration curve can also be used to determine the equilibrium constant (K_a) for a weak acid (see Figure 9.2 on the following page). At the point where half of the volume of base has been added to reach the equivalence point, half of the acid has been converted to its conjugate base. Therefore the concentration of remaining acid is equal to the concentration of conjugate base present. At this point (the ½ equivalence point), $pH = pK_a$, as can be seen when you consider the K_a expression for the weak acid.

$$K_a = \frac{[H_3O^+][A^-]}{[HA]}$$

at the ½ equivalence point,

$$[HA] = [A^-]$$

$$\text{so } K_a = [H_3O^+]$$

$$\text{and } pK_a = pH$$

Thus K_a can by calculated using the expression $K_a = 10^{-pK_a}$.

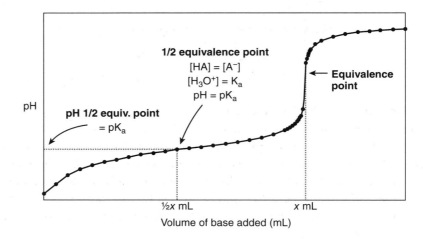

Figure 9.2. pH titration curve for the titration of a weak acid with a strong base.

More information about acid–base titrations, equivalence points, and the use of indicators can be found in your textbook.

Part I. Analysis of Acids Using a Base

Acetic Acid: The Acid in Vinegar

Although stomach acid contains hydrochloric acid, a strong acid, most acids found in biological systems are weak acids. Among the simplest of these acids is acetic acid, CH_3COOH, the component that gives white vinegar its sharp odor and sour taste. Other types of vinegar are also solutions of acetic acid but they contain other compounds which give them various colors and more complex flavors.

All commercial vinegars are required by law to contain at least 4% by weight of acetic acid. If we examine the ingredients on the label of a bottle of vinegar, we generally find that the vinegar contains about 5% by weight of acetic acid in water (often listed as "5% Acidity").

Prelab

As part of your individual preparation for lab, read the experiment and answer the following questions in your lab notebook before going to lab. The copy of your answers on perforated pages from your lab notebook is due at the beginning of lab.

1.   A 10.00-mL sample of a solution containing a monoprotic weak acid was placed in a 100-mL volumetric flask, diluted to the mark with water and mixed well. A 25.00-mL aliquot of this **diluted** acid solution was then titrated with NaOH. If the titration required 17.23 mL of 0.09913 M NaOH to reach the equivalence point, calculate the molarity of the acid in the dilute and the original solution (that is, before dilution).

2.   In a titration of a monoprotic weak acid with sodium hydroxide, the pH at the half-equivalence point is 3.81.

   •   What are the values of pK_a and K_a for the acid?

   •   Is the pH at the equivalence point less than, equal to, or greater than 7.0? Explain.

3.   Consider a titration carried out using 30.0 mL of 0.015 M HA ($K_a = 3.0 \times 10^{-5}$) that required 34.8 mL of NaOH solution to reach the equivalence point.

   a.   The pH of the weak acid solution before any NaOH is added is based on the weak acid equilibrium system.

   $$HA(aq) + H_2O(\ell) \rightleftharpoons H_3O^+(aq) + A^-(aq)$$

   Calculate the $[H_3O^+]$ and $[A^-]$ in the weak acid solution.

   b.   Calculate the molarity of the NaOH solution used in the titration.

4.   Vinegar solutions are often labeled as being 5% by mass "acidity." Assuming that the density of vinegar is equal to the density of water, calculate the molarity of "acidity" in the vinegar.

5.   In your laboratory notebook, record the experimental procedure you will follow in lab. The procedure is your experimental plan and can be organized as an outline, a flowchart, or a numbered list of steps. You should also include a statement of the purpose of the experiment, notes on safety, and a reference to the relevant pages in your laboratory manual. The copy of your procedure on the duplicate pages of your lab notebook is due at the beginning of lab.

NOTES

Experimental Design

In the first titration sequence, you will titrate a solution of hydrochloric acid of known concentration with a sodium hydroxide solution of unknown concentration and calculate the concentration of sodium hydroxide.

Then, in the second titration sequence, you will use this standardized sodium hydroxide solution to titrate and determine the concentration of acetic acid in the vinegar. **The vinegar is too concentrated to titrate directly, so you must titrate a carefully diluted solution.**

Each group is to complete a minimum of three titrations of each acid: two colorimetric and one pH titration. Groups should split into two subgroups to collect data as outlined in the table below. The subgroups will compare the results obtained from the two titration methods.

	Subgroup A	Subgroup B
Titration: Strong Acid with Strong Base	Does the **colorimetric titrations and corresponding calculations** while subgroup B does titration with Logger *Pro*.	Does the **pH titration with Logger *Pro*** while subgroup A does the colorimetric titrations and calculations.
Titration: Diluted Weak Acid with Strong Base	Does the pH **titration with Logger *Pro*** while subgroup B does the colorimetric titrations and calculations.	Does the **colorimetric titrations and corresponding calculations** while subgroup A does titration with Logger *Pro*.

Data Collection

Lab work is done in groups. Each person must record a complete set of data for solution preparation and traditional titrations in his/her lab notebook and turn in the copy on the perforated pages from the lab notebook at the end of lab.

Each group is allotted 300 mL of NaOH solution of unknown concentration, 100 mL of standardized HCl, and 20 mL of the assigned commercial vinegar. Buffers are reused.

NEVER pipet directly from the reagent bottle! Pour a sample of the solution to be measured into a clean beaker and pipet from the beaker.

 Review proper use of volumetric measuring techniques (burets, pipets, etc.) in How to Be Successful in CHM 12901: A Guide to Using Laboratory Equipment and Instrumentation at the beginning of this manual.

All volumes should be reported to 2 decimal places. (Graduated cylinders should not be used for measuring in this experiment.)

Titrate Strong Acid with Strong Base

NOTES

Goal: Determine the exact concentration of NaOH in a NaOH solution by titrating it with standardized HCl.

Colorimetric Titration

- Using a clean, rinsed pipet, measure exactly 25.00 mL of the HCl solution into a clean 125-mL Erlenmeyer flask. Add one or two drops of phenolphthalein to the acid.

- Either set up a magnetic stir plate or plan to swirl the flask throughout the titration.

- Support a 50.00-mL buret on a ring stand with a buret clamp. Fill the buret with NaOH *before* setting it over the flask containing HCl. For each new titration the buret must be filled with titrant so that the volume reading is near 0.00 mL.

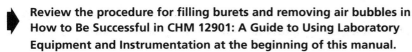 **Review the procedure for filling burets and removing air bubbles in How to Be Successful in CHM 12901: A Guide to Using Laboratory Equipment and Instrumentation at the beginning of this manual.**

- Position the buret so that the stream from the buret can be directed into the flask on a magnetic stir plate, if using one.

- "Scout" titration: With stirring, add NaOH from the buret to the acid sample until the color changes from colorless to light pink and the color persists for 15–30 seconds. Record all necessary measurements.

- Careful titration: Repeat with a second sample of HCl, adding the NaOH more slowly this time to get an accurate volume measurement.

pH Titration

Instrumentation can be a great advance in data collection. However, it seems that any gain in accuracy and precision is offset by additional time needed to care for, calibrate, and operate the equipment along with an increase in cost. At the current time, the cost to replace a pH electrode of the type you will use is $100.

Care and Handling of pH Electrodes

- Keep the electrode moist (wet) at all times. When you are not using the electrode, it should be in electrode storage solution or deionized water. Be sure the electrode is stored properly when you have finished using it.

- When you move the electrode from one solution to another, move the beakers carefully without touching the electrode. The electrode has a thin membrane at the bottom that is easily broken.

- Never dry an electrode by rubbing it with a paper towel. Just "dab" water droplets with a lint-free paper such as a Kimwipe or AccuWipe.

- When using a magnetic stirring bar do not allow it to hit the electrode.

NOTES

Calibration of the Electrode

You must calibrate the equipment for a pH titration. As you go through the calibration procedure below, the display will not show a reasonable pH value that corresponds to the pH of the buffer solutions until *both* buffers have been used for the calibration process.

You only need to recalibrate the equipment if you need a different pH range for a titration or if you turn off the equipment. Since we are titrating a sample of acid in both experiments, you will not need to recalibrate between titrations.

The pH electrode is kept in a tube of storage solution next to the computer; connect it to the LabQuest 2 interface via the port labeled CH1. Then connect the LabQuest interface to the computer via the mini USB port. Plug in the LabQuest using the power adapter. Turn on LabQuest.

Open the Logger *Pro* program, which you will use to record pH and volume of base added as you perform pH titrations. The LabQuest interface should display the LabQuest logo as an indication that the equipment is connected correctly.

You will need jars of pH 4 and 10 buffer for a two-point calibration of the electrode. Use the buffer solutions in the jars provided. Do not transfer the buffer solutions to another container. Do not discard the buffer solutions.

1. On the toolbar, click **Experiment** > **Calibrate** > **LabQuest 2: 1 CH1: pH**. This will open a new window called **Sensor Settings**. Click **Calibrate Now**.

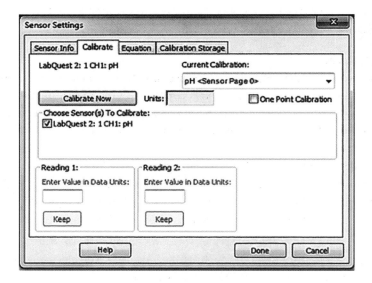

2. Remove the pH electrode from the storage solution. Rinse the electrode with deionized water (use a small beaker to collect the rinses), blot it dry using a Kimwipe and place the electrode in the pH 4 buffer solution. Swirl the jar gently for 15 seconds. In the box for **Reading 1:** enter a value of "**4**" and click **Keep** to store the calibration point.

3. Remove the electrode from the pH 4 buffer, rinse it with deionized water and blot dry. Place the electrode in the pH 10 buffer solution and swirl gently for 15 seconds. Enter "**10**" as the value for **Reading 2** and click **Keep** to store the second calibration point. Click **Done** to exit the Sensor Settings window.

4. Remove the electrode from the buffer, rinse with deionized water and place the electrode in the tube of storage solution or deionized water. Your pH electrode is now calibrated.

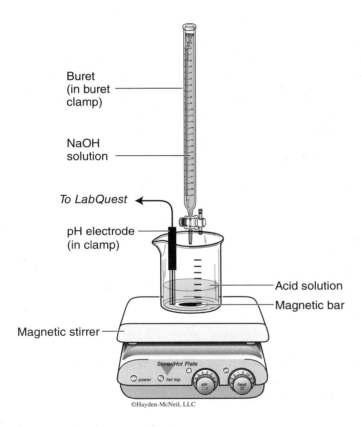

Buret (in buret clamp)

NaOH solution

To LabQuest

pH electrode (in clamp)

Acid solution

Magnetic bar

Magnetic stirrer

Stirrer/Hot Plate

power   hot top   stir   heat

©Hayden-McNeil, LLC

Figure 9.3. pH titration setup.

pH Titration

▶ **Check with the subgroup doing the colorimetric titration to find out the volume of NaOH needed to reach the equivalence point.**

•   Pipet 25.00 mL of acid into a clean beaker containing a magnetic stir bar. Add enough deionized water (about 10–15 mL) so that the tip of the pH electrode is immersed and far enough above the magnetic stir bar that the stir bar won't hit the electrode. Set the beaker on a magnetic stir plate next to the computer.

NOTES

- Support a 50.00-mL buret on a ring stand. Fill the buret with NaOH before setting it over the beaker containing HCl. For each new titration the buret must be filled with titrant so that the volume reading is near 0.00 mL.

▶ **Review the procedure for filling burets and removing air bubbles in How to Be Successful in CHM 12901: A Guide to Using Laboratory Equipment and Instrumentation at the beginning of this manual.**

- Adjust the 50.00-mL buret filled with NaOH so that the stream from the buret can be directed into the beaker on the magnetic stir plate.

- Adjust the stirring rate to a moderate rotation speed.

Collecting pH Titration Data with the Logger *Pro* Program

The default setting for the Logger *Pro* program is to collect data at time intervals, but for a titration, you will want to collect the pH data and compare it to the volume of titrant instead. Change this setting by clicking on **Experiment > Data Collection**. From the **Mode** drop-down menu, select **Events With Entry**. Enter the following in the corresponding fields:

Column Name	enter "volume"
Short Name	enter "vol"
Units	enter "mL"

Click **Done**.

The pH value will be displayed in the lower left corner of the screen. Change the scale of the x-axis to 0–40 mL by clicking on the maximum volume and changing it to 40 mL.

To begin collecting titration data:

1. Click 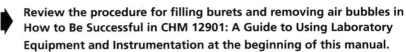 . When the pH stabilizes, click ⊛ keep . You will be prompted to enter the cumulative volume of sodium hydroxide that has been dispensed by the buret.

   For your first measurement, you will enter 0.00, because no sodium hydroxide solution has been added. For subsequent measurements, you will enter the total change in volume (final volume – initial volume). For example, if you begin your titration with an initial buret reading of 5.50 mL, then add sodium hydroxide solution until the buret reads 6.70 mL, you will enter 1.20 mL (6.70 – 5.50) into Logger *Pro*. For your next reading, if you add sodium hydroxide until 8.30 mL, you will enter 2.80 mL (8.30 – 5.50).

   If you make a mistake while entering the volume, you can edit the entry by double-clicking on the value in the data table.

   After each addition of NaOH allow the pH to stabilize before clicking **Keep**. If you erroneously click **Keep** before the pH has stabilized, the entry can be deleted. Click on the corresponding volume in the data table and delete the entry. This should remove the data point from your graph. If you stop the data collection prematurely, click **Collect** again and choose **Append Run** to continue recording data.

2. Begin the titration by adding the solution of unknown base to the acid about 1 mL at a time until you are within 1–2 mL of the equivalence point as determined by your subgroup's results. Then as the endpoint is approached and the pH begins to change significantly, decrease the addition of base to **2 drops at a time**. Do this part rather quickly since prolonged stirring introduces CO_2 from the air and will change the pH of the solution.

3. When you are 1 mL past the equivalence point, return to adding NaOH about 1 mL at a time until you are approximately 10 mL beyond the equivalence point.

4. When you have finished the titration, press 　 ▣ stop 　. Rinse the electrode and immerse it in the tube of storage solution. Pour the titrated solution down the drain. BE CAREFUL: Do not drop the magnetic stirring bar down the drain. Rinse the magnetic stirring bar with deionized water for reuse.

Saving Your Data

1. If you are performing your data analysis in the lab using Logger *Pro* (suggested), choose **Save As** from the **File** drop-down menu. Give your data an appropriate file name and save to the desired destination.

2. If you will analyze your data away from the lab, choose **Export As** from the **File** drop-down menu and select **Text…**. Give your data an appropriate file name and save to the desired destination. This will allow you to open your data with Excel or some other spreadsheet program. *You will not have access to the Logger **Pro** software outside of lab, so make sure that any data you need, including any plots of the first or second derivative, are exported rather than saved.* **See Plotting the Derivative later**.

3. Choose **Clear all Data** from the **Data** drop-down menu.

NOTES

Titrate the Weak Acid in Vinegar with Strong Base

Goals

- Determine the concentration of acetic acid in

    - a diluted solution of a commercial vinegar, and

    - the original, undiluted, commercial vinegar using the NaOH solution standardized in the previous procedure.

- Determine an experimental value for K_a of acetic acid.

Final Step to Prepare Dilute Solution in Volumetric Flask

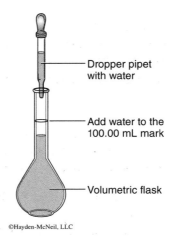

Dropper pipet with water

Add water to the 100.00 mL mark

Volumetric flask

©Hayden-McNeil, LLC

Figure 9.4.

Because commercial vinegar is too concentrated to titrate directly you will need to prepare a diluted solution.

 Review of proper volumetric measuring techniques can be found in How to Be Successful in CHM 12901: A Guide to Using Laboratory Equipment and Instrumentation at the beginning of this manual.

Prepare the diluted solution as follows:

- Use a beaker to obtain about 20 mL of the vinegar brand assigned to your group.

- Use a 10.00-mL volumetric pipet to transfer 10.00 mL of vinegar from the beaker to a 100.00-mL volumetric flask.

- Add some deionized water to the flask and mix well, then carefully fill the flask to the mark with deionized water and mix well again. (To mix, cover the flask with a small square of Parafilm and invert several times.) Do not add any additional water to the flask.

- What is the dilution factor for this dilution?

NOTES

In this experiment, you will use the same techniques that you used for titrating a strong acid with a strong base but this time you'll be titrating a weak acid.

Perform two colorimetric titrations and one pH titration with the standardized NaOH solution to determine the concentration of acetic acid in the diluted vinegar solution. Use 25.00-mL samples of the **diluted** vinegar solution for the titrations. Follow the same general procedure you used for the titration of a strong acid with a strong base.

Cleanup and Storage of Equipment
- Rinse the stir bar and return it to your instructor. BE CAREFUL: Do not pour the magnetic stir bar into the sink with the solution.

- Rinse all glassware at least three times with deionized water. Return equipment to your instructor or the appropriate location.

- Disconnect the pH electrode and return it to the tube of storage solution. Shut down the LabQuest interface and return it and the adapter to the box on your bench. Close the Logger *Pro* program.

- Keep your splash goggles on until you have completed the data analysis, turned in your report, and are leaving the lab. Lock your lab drawer before leaving lab.

Data Analysis

Strong Acid with Strong Base Titrations
Write the balanced chemical equation to represent the acid–base reaction that occurred in the titration of a strong acid with strong base.

Numerical Analysis Component (using data from the colorimetric titration)
Use data from the careful colorimetric titration to calculate the molarity of NaOH in the NaOH solution. (You can review the fundamentals of solution stoichiometry calculations in your textbook.)

Graphical Analysis Component (using data from the pH titration)
- Print a graph of "pH" vs. "Volume of Base Added" on a separate sheet.

- Use one of the graphical methods described in the introduction of this lab to determine the volume of sodium hydroxide added at the equivalence point. Plotting the derivative is explained later. You may need to expand the x-axis of your graph to get a more accurate volume reading.

- On the printed graph identify and label the equivalence point and volume of titrant at the equivalence point.

NOTES

Plotting the Derivative

To calculate and plot the first or second derivative data:

1. Click on **Data > New Calculated Column**. Provide an appropriate title for the new column in the **Name** and **Short Name** boxes such as second derivative and d2.

2. Click inside the **Expression** box; then click **Functions**. Select the appropriate function (**calculus > derivative** or **calculus > secondDerivative**).

3. The variables are separated by a comma with the y-variable first then x-variable. Choose **Variables (Columns) > pH**. Type a comma (,) then click **Variables (Columns) > volume**. Click **Done**.

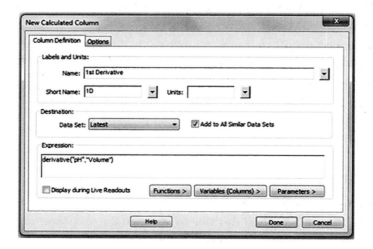

To view the graph of the derivative and find the equivalence point:

1. Select or highlight the derivative column on the data table, then click **Insert > Graph**.

2. You can expand the x-axis within a small range before and after the equivalence point and find the volume of NaOH added to within two places beyond the decimal. Click and drag on the graph to select portions of the curve (see the following figure). Your selection should include the maximum of the first derivative graph or the region between the maximum and minimum if you are using the second derivative graph.

3. Click **Zoom In**, to expand the axes and find the mL of sodium hydroxide added to reach the equivalence point.

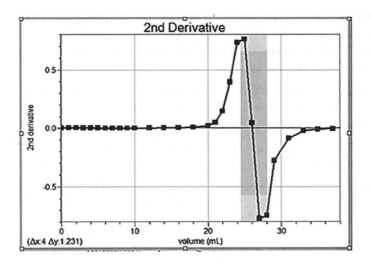

Numerical Analysis Component (using data from the pH titration)

Use information obtained from the graph to calculate the concentration of the NaOH in the strong base solution.

Weak Acid with Strong Base Titrations

Write the balanced chemical equation to represent the acid–base reaction that occurred in the titration of the weak acid with strong base.

Numerical Analysis Component (using data from the colorimetric titration)

Use data from the careful colorimetric titration and the molarity of NaOH determined in the previous careful colorimetric titration to calculate the molarity of acetic acid in the dilute vinegar solution. Then calculate the molarity of acetic acid in the original commercial vinegar. (Use the dilution factor you determined earlier.)

Graphical Analysis Component (using data from the pH titration)

- Print a graph of "Volume of Base Added" on a separate sheet.

- Use one of the methods described in the introduction of this lab to determine the volume of sodium hydroxide added at the equivalence point. You may need to expand the x-axis of your graph to get a more accurate volume reading. See Plotting the Derivative previously.

- Use the mL of sodium hydroxide at the equivalence point to find the volume of NaOH at the 1/2 equivalence point on the titration curve. Determine the pK_a of acetic acid from the graph.

- On the printed graph identify and label the equivalence point, volume of sodium hydroxide at the equivalence point, volume of sodium hydroxide at the 1/2 equivalence point, and the pK_a.

NOTES

Numerical Analysis Component (using data from the pH titration)

- Using the data obtained from the graph and the concentration of the NaOH determined potentiometrically, calculate the concentration of the acetic acid in the dilute vinegar solution.

- Calculate the concentration of the vinegar before it was diluted (i.e., the original commercial vinegar). (Use the dilution factor you determined earlier.)

- Calculate an experimental value of the % by mass "acidity" in the vinegar brand you analyzed.

- Determine the K_a value for the weak acid, acetic acid. (Refer to the information given in the introduction.) Identify and label information on the graph to illustrate how you obtained the values for $[H_3O^+]$ and ½ equivalence point.

Results

Summarize the experiment results your group obtained.

Calculate the % error of your experimental K_a value for acetic acid with the accepted value listed in your textbook.

$$\% \text{ error} = \frac{|\text{experimental} - \text{actual}|}{\text{actual}} \times 100$$

Postlab Questions

1. Obtain the actual NaOH concentration value from your TA and calculate the % error for each of the titration methods (colorimetric and pH). Based on your results, is one titration method more accurate than the other? What are the benefits and disadvantages of using pH titrations instead of the colorimetric method?

2. Compare the titration curves of weak acid–strong base reactions with the curve for strong acid–strong base reactions. How are they similar? How are they different?

3. In your data analysis, you did not take the added volume of water into consideration when calculating the original acid concentration. Why not?

4. Explain the effect of each of the following on the precision or accuracy of the concentration of acetic acid in vinegar and K_a for acetic acid. Indicate in each case whether you would expect the experimental results to be falsely high or falsely low.

   a. The pipet used to measure the HCl was rinsed only with deionized water before measuring the acid.

   b. The dilute vinegar sample was added to a wet beaker.

c. A large air bubble that you did not observe at the beginning of a titration of dilute vinegar was present in the buret tip at the end of the titration.

d. The buret was rinsed with deionized water only before it was filled with the NaOH solution.

Lab Records and Reports

Group Portion
Remember that it is your responsibility as a group to ensure that everyone whose name is on the report has participated as fully as possible in the completion of the project.

Individual Portion
Each student must attach laboratory notebook duplicate pages containing a complete data set and observations for the experiment.

NOTES

CHAPTER 10

Acid–Base Equilibria: Analyses of Polyprotic Acids

10

In this laboratory activity you will plan and then carry out titrations to analyze or characterize oxalic acid and a solid weak acid. You will use the same techniques as those used in the previous chapter; that is, colorimetric and pH titrations. When planning your analysis, you must take into consideration that oxalic acid is a diprotic acid, but the unknown solid weak acid may be a mono- or diprotic acid.

Prelab

As part of your individual preparation for lab, read the experiment and answer the following questions in your lab notebook before going to lab. The copy of your answers on perforated pages from your lab notebook is due at the beginning of lab.

1. A student titrated a 15.00-mL sample of a solution containing a monoprotic weak acid with NaOH. If the titration required 13.36 mL of 0.1015 M NaOH to reach the equivalence point, calculate:

    *   molarity of acid in the sample

    *   mass (in g) of acid in the sample if the molecular mass of the acid is 60.00 g/mol

2. Sketch a pH titration curve for a diprotic acid. Identify and label the parts or portions of the curve where you will obtain information used to:

    *   calculate the molarity of the acid

    * K_{a1}

    * K_{a2}

3. In your laboratory notebook, record the experimental procedure you will follow in lab. The procedure is your experimental plan and can be organized as an outline, a flowchart, or a numbered list of steps. You should

NOTES

also include a statement of the purpose of the experiment, notes on safety, and a reference to the relevant pages in your laboratory manual. The copy of your procedure on the duplicate pages of your lab notebook is due at the beginning of lab.

Lab work is done in groups. Each person must (1) record a complete set of data for solution preparation and colorimetric titrations in his/her lab notebook and turn in the copy on the perforated pages from the lab notebook at the end of lab and (2) have a complete set of pH titration data on an electronic storage device before leaving lab.

Additional Information to Consider When Planning and Carrying Out Your Procedures

- Use the same methods and equipment used in the previous chapter to carry out the titrations described in the goals.

- Review the information and graphs about acid–base titrations in your textbook.

- Titrations are to be done beginning with 25.00-mL samples of the desired solution in a beaker or flask with an additional 10–15 mL of deionized water to increase the volume.

- Indicators signal the equivalence point of a titration by a change in physical property, such as color. Phenolphthalein changes color in the pH 8–10 range and works well to signal the equivalence point of reactions between strong acids or weak acids with strong bases.

- pH titrations are done without color indicators because color indicators often have acid–base properties of their own and can change the pH values slightly.

- Carry out pH titrations of the oxalic acid and unknown solid weak acid using small increments of base throughout the entire process in order to avoid adding too much base and possibly missing the first equivalence point should the acid be diprotic.

- pH titration curves for diprotic acids show two sigmoidal regions if the K_a values differ by several orders of magnitude.

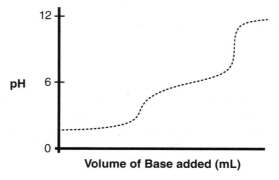

Figure 10.1. pH titration curve of diprotic acid with base.

Titrating Oxalic Acid with Strong Base

Each group has been allotted 100 mL of oxalic acid and 150 mL of standardized NaOH to complete the analyses.

Goals: Your group will design and carry out procedures to

- Titrate **25.00-mL samples of oxalic acid** in two ways (colorimetrically and potentiometrically).

- Calculate and compare the concentration of the acid in the oxalic acid solution using data from both titration methods.

- Determine experimental values for K_{a1} and K_{a2} for oxalic acid.

Titrating an Unknown Solid Weak Acid with Strong Base

Your group will first prepare 100 mL of a solution containing an unknown weak acid. Do this by dissolving ~0.7 g (weigh and record to the nearest 0.001 g) of the acid in water in a 100-mL beaker. Add approximately 25 mL of deionized water to the beaker and swirl to dissolve the solid. Carefully, transfer the solution to a 100.0-mL volumetric flask. Rinse the walls and bottom of the beaker twice with deionized water and transfer to the volumetric flask. Cover the flask with Parafilm and invert several times to dissolve the solid. Add water exactly to the 100-mL mark on the flask; cover with Parafilm and mix.

Each group has been allotted 180 mL of NaOH solution to complete the analysis.

Goals: Your group will design and carry out procedures to

- Titrate 25.00-mL samples of the weak acid solution colorimetrically and potentiometrically.

- Determine if the "unknown" acid is monoprotic (HA) or diprotic (H_2A) in nature.

  monoprotic
  $$HA + H_2O \rightleftharpoons H_3O^+ + A^- \qquad K_a$$

  diprotic
  $$H_2A + H_2O \rightleftharpoons H_3O^+ + HA^- \qquad K_{a1}$$
  $$HA^- + H_2O \rightleftharpoons H_3O^+ + A^{2-} \qquad K_{a2}$$

- Calculate and compare the concentration of acid in the solution using data from both titration methods.

- Calculate the molecular weight of the "unknown" acid.

- Determine the K_a value(s) for the acid.

  That is: K_a if the acid is monoprotic; K_{a1} and K_{a2} if the acid is diprotic.

  $$K_{a1} = \frac{[H_3O^+][HA^-]}{[H_2A]} \qquad K_{a2} = \frac{[H_3O^+][A^{2-}]}{[HA^-]}$$

Cleanup and Storage of Equipment

- Rinse the stir bar and return it to your instructor. BE CAREFUL: Do not pour the magnetic stir bar into the sink with the solution.

- Rinse all glassware at least three times with deionized water. Return equipment to your instructor or the appropriate location.

- Make sure the pH electrode is stored properly in deionized water or storage solution.

- Turn off the LabQuest interface by selecting the Home icon then System > Shut down > OK. Return the power adapter and LabQuest to the box on your bench.

- Keep your splash goggles on until you have completed collecting data and are leaving the lab. Lock your lab drawer before leaving lab.

Data Analysis

Titrating Oxalic Acid with Strong Base

Write the balanced chemical equation to represent the acid–base reaction that occurred in the titration of oxalic acid with strong base.

Numerical Analysis Component (Using Data from the Colorimetric Titration)

Use data from the careful colorimetric titration to calculate the molarity of oxalic acid.

Graphical Analysis Component (Using Data from the pH Titration)

Print a graph of "pH" versus "Volume of Base Added." Use one of the methods described in the previous chapter to determine the volume of base added to reach the equivalence points. Identify and label the equivalence points and volume of sodium hydroxide at the equivalence points on the graph.

Numerical Analysis Component (Using Data from the pH Titration)

Using the data obtained from the graph, calculate the concentration of the oxalic acid.

Identify and label information on the graph to illustrate how you obtained the values for ½ equivalence point and the pK_{a1} and pK_{a2}. Determine the K_{a1} and K_{a2} values for the oxalic acid.

Titrating an Unknown Solid Weak Acid with Strong Base

Graphical Analysis Component (Using Data from the pH Titration)

Print a graph of "pH" versus "Volume of Base Added." Use one of the methods described in the previous chapter to determine the volume of base added to reach the equivalence point(s). Identify and label the equivalence point(s) and volume of titrant at the equivalence point(s).

From the graph, determine if the "unknown" acid is monoprotic or diprotic.

Numerical Analysis Component (Using Data from the Colorimetric Titration)
Use data from the careful colorimetric titration and the molarity of the NaOH to calculate the molarity of the unknown acid solution.

Numerical Analysis Component (Using Data from the pH Titration)
Using the data obtained from the graph, calculate the concentration of the unknown weak acid solution. Use the concentration and mass of unknown solid used to make the solution to calculate the molecular weight of the unknown acid.

Identify and label information on the graph to illustrate how you obtained the values for ½ equivalence point and the pK_a(s).

Results
Summarize the experimental results your group obtained. Compare your experimental K values for oxalic acid with the accepted values of $pK_{a1} = 1.46$ and $pK_{a2} = 4.40$ by calculating the % error in your experimental values. Your teaching assistant will give you the identity and the published value for ionization constant(s) for the unknown solid weak acid. Compare your experimental values for the molecular weight and K_a(s) with the accepted values by calculating the % error in your experimental values.

Postlab Questions
Answer the following questions in your lab report.

1. Why is it necessary to use a buffer solution to calibrate a pH electrode or meter? Why isn't deionized H_2O used? Be specific with your reasons.

2. In the titration of oxalic acid with sodium hydroxide, what is the pH at the equivalence points? What chemical species are in solution at these points, and how do they account for the pH?

Lab Records and Reports

Group Portion
Remember that it is your responsibility as a group to ensure that everyone whose name is on the report has participated as fully as possible in the completion of the project.

Individual Portion
Each student must attach laboratory notebook duplicate pages containing a complete data set and observations for the experiment.

NOTES

pH and Buffers

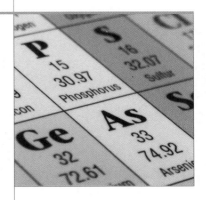

Purpose

The concentration of hydrogen ions in solution, or pH, is of great importance to living systems. Since both cell structure and function can be affected by even small changes in pH, maintaining pH within a narrow range is a major goal of cellular homeostasis. The human body maintains homeostasis with a complex physiological system of buffers in the blood, kidneys and cells. The buffer systems lessen or moderate the impact of an increase or decrease in pH. During this laboratory, we will concentrate on the maintenance of the blood pH. You will prepare simulated blood and investigate how to manipulate the blood buffer system.

In a hospital emergency room, a patient has just been wheeled in following a cardiac arrest in his home. The paramedics were able to restart his heart after a couple of minutes, and prior to that, CPR was administered so that enough oxygen flowed to his tissues to keep them alive. But his face has the ashen color of someone close to death, and his skin is cold. Though his heart is beating again, he is in danger of death from shock. Immediately, one emergency room nurse starts to prepare an intravenous tube, and another gets a bag of fluid from the supply cabinet. The doctor says, "Yes, let's start him on bicarb" and the nurse begins to administer the fluid, one that helps to restore the victim's blood to its normal state and prevents further damage.

The fluid the ER team has just used to stabilize the patient is the same one that you might use to quiet an upset stomach. It is sodium hydrogen carbonate (or bicarbonate of soda, also known as bicarb or baking soda). The formula of sodium hydrogen carbonate, $NaHCO_3$, is quite simple, but its role in the body is profound. The hydrogen carbonate ion, HCO_3^-, is a weak base that works with its conjugate weak acid carbonic acid, H_2CO_3, to form a stable pH buffer in the blood. This keeps the blood at a constant pH, something that is essential for life.

$$H^+ + HCO_3^- \rightleftharpoons H_2CO_3$$

NOTES

The pH of the blood of healthy adults is usually between 7.35 and 7.45. This is maintained by a 1:20 ratio of H_2CO_3:HCO_3^-. Very small changes in the amount of either substance can radically alter the pH and result in illness and death. Some of these changes are associated with problems in breathing, such as pneumonia and hyperventilation. In this experiment, however, we will be more concerned with a patient with metabolic problems.

If the ratio of carbonic acid to hydrogen carbonate becomes too low, the blood pH will rise and the body will become alkalotic. This can happen when vomiting occurs, resulting in the body compensating by utilizing carbonic acid from the blood to reestablish the stomach acid.

The ratio of carbonic acid to hydrogen carbonate can also be too high, which happens when excess acid is present in the body. When excess acid is present, the blood pH drops and the body becomes acidotic. Acidosis occurs when the body is unable to remove carbon dioxide because the blood stops circulating during cardiac arrest. Different forms of acidosis and alkalosis and their relative pHs can be seen in Figure 11.1.

When the body starts to become alkalotic or acidotic, there is a time period where the proper pH can be restored by the body's natural response. This process is known as compensation by the blood. Compensation for pH problems does not correct the ultimate source of the imbalance, but it can prevent other problems from arising.

Certain events cause such dramatic and threatening pH changes that we cannot wait for natural compensation. When a cardiac arrest occurs, the blood stops moving through the body. Immediately, the concentration of carbonic acid starts to rise, lowering the pH. In addition, normal metabolism halts and lactic acid (the product of partial metabolism of carbohydrates) starts to accumulate, causing a further lowering of the pH. Even after the heart is restarted, the change in the blood's buffer may be so severe that it places the patient in grave danger. Administration of hydrogen carbonate is sometimes the only way to prevent further, perhaps fatal, damage from occurring. Consequently, an understanding of blood pH and buffers is essential to proper methods in the emergency room.

In this experiment, you will progress from studying how buffers work to the point where you are ready to simulate the time-sensitive nature of administering bicarb in the emergency room.

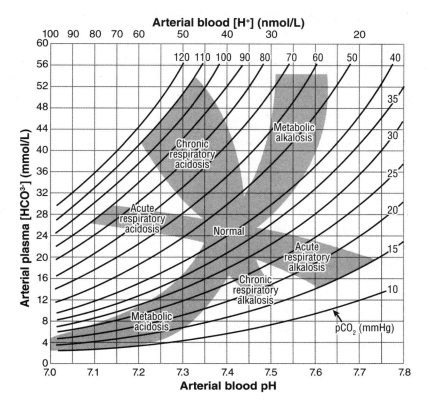

Figure 11.1. Arterial blood pH in different forms of acidosis and alkalosis.

Prelab

As part of your individual preparation for lab, read the experiment and answer the following questions in your lab notebook before going to lab. The copy of your answers is due at the beginning of lab.

1. Determine the number of moles of reagent in the following solutions:

    a. 25.00 mL of 0.10 M acetic acid

    b. 5.55 mL of 0.092 M NaOH

2. A buffer solution contains 0.120 M acetic acid and 0.150 M sodium acetate.

    a. How many moles of acetic acid and sodium acetate are present in 50.0 mL of solution?

    b. If we add 5.55 mL of 0.092 M NaOH to the solution in part (a), how many moles of acetic acid, sodium acetate, and NaOH will be present after the reaction has finished?

    c. If we add 0.50 mL of 0.087 M HCl to the solution in part (a), how many moles of acetic acid, sodium acetate, and HCl will be present after the reaction is complete?

3. Determine the pH you expect to find for the three solutions in question 2.

4. If you need to prepare 250.0 mL of a pH 5.00 buffer that has a total buffer concentration of acetic acid + sodium acetate of 0.050 M, how many moles of each will you need to prepare the solution? Given solutions of acetic acid and sodium acetate with concentrations of 0.10 M and $pK_a = 4.76$, describe how to prepare this buffer.

5. Assume that the normal blood buffer contains 0.00080 M carbonic acid and 0.0090 M hydrogen carbonate; the $pK_a = 6.35$ for carbonic acid and the volume of blood in the body is 7.00 L. The blood pH, due to disruption, is now 7.20. What is the ratio of $[HCO_3^-]/[H_2CO_3]$ now that the blood has been challenged? How many moles of hydrogen carbonate must be added to the blood to bring the carbonic acid/hydrogen carbonate ratio back to a normal pH = 7.4? How many milliliters of 0.10 M hydrogen carbonate must be added to the blood?

6. In your laboratory notebook, record the experimental procedure you will follow in lab. **HINT: It will be extremely helpful to calculate how much acid and base are needed to make your buffer in the procedure of the lab ahead of time (see Part I of the procedure).**

Buffers

Physiological processes require that pH remain relatively constant. The pH of the blood in our bodies must be within a very small range and is maintained between 7.35 and 7.45 despite many imbalances. For instance, our bodies are constantly correcting imbalances in the blood pH due to normal processes such as cellular respiration that produces CO_2 which the blood picks up from the tissues and returns to the heart. Our diets and the normal metabolic reactions in cells may contribute an excess of hydrogen ions. The pH must be kept constant by several *buffer systems*.

A buffer is defined as a solution that resists change in pH when small amounts of acid or base are added. A complex and tightly controlled equilibrium process between bicarbonate, phosphate, and protein buffer systems maintain our blood pH. We will use the phosphate buffer system as an illustration.

A buffer is made by mixing a weak acid with its salt (conjugate base) in order to make a solution that can act as an acid (give up hydrogen ions) and as a base (accept hydrogen ions). In a sodium phosphate buffer, the weak acid, $H_2PO_4^-$, is supplied as NaH_2PO_4 (sodium dihydrogen phosphate) and its salt as Na_2HPO_4 (sodium monohydrogen phosphate).

At equilibrium, these substances are ionized to some degree.

$$NaH_2PO_4 \rightleftharpoons Na^+ + H_2PO_4^-$$

$$NaH_2PO_4 \rightleftharpoons Na^+ + HPO_4^{2-}$$

If hydrogen ions are added to the solution, they can be picked up by HPO_4^{2-}, which acts as a base:

$$H^+ + HPO_4^{2-} \rightleftharpoons H_2PO_4^-$$

If hydroxyl (OH^-) ions are added to the solution, they can be picked up by $H_2PO_4^-$:

$$OH^- + H_2PO_4^- \rightleftharpoons HPO_4^{2-} + H_2O$$

In summary,

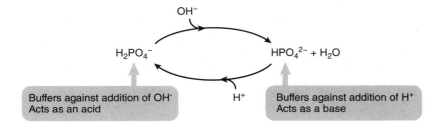

pH of a Buffer

For an acid–base buffer of intermediate pH ranges (between 2 and 11), the pH is controlled by the equilibrium between the weak acid, HA; its conjugate base, A^-; and the H^+ concentrations. The analysis of the equilibrium concentrations involves the dissociation constant expression, K_a:

$$K_a = \frac{[H^+][A^-]}{[HA]}$$

If we are interested in weak acids with dissociation constants that are less than 10^{-3}, the Henderson–Hasselbalch equation can be used to calculate the pH of a buffer. This equation is derived by rearranging the dissociation expression to solve for $[H^+]$:

$$[H^+] = \frac{K_a[HA]}{[A^-]}$$

We then take the negative logarithm of both sides of the equation and rearrange the expression to obtain the Henderson–Hasselbalch equation.

$$pH = pK_a + \log\frac{[A^-]}{[HA]}$$

The Henderson–Hasselbalch equation is very helpful in calculating the concentrations of a weak acid and conjugate base needed to prepare a buffer with a desired pH. Given the pK_a of a weak acid and the desired pH range, the ratio of conjugate base and weak acid can easily be calculated.

How Does a Buffer Moderate pH?

There are three types of "stress" that can be applied to a buffer: (a) dilution, (b) addition of strong acid, and (c) addition of strong base. Buffers can resist these stresses and the Henderson–Hasselbalch equation illustrates how buffers resist changes in pH.

Dilution

If 0.100 L of buffer contains 0.025 M HA and 0.050 M A⁻, then the ratio $[A^-]/[HA]$ is 2.0. Assume the pK_a of HA is 4.00. We use the Henderson–Hasselbalch equation to calculate the pH

$$pH = 4.00 + \log(2.0) = 4.00 + 0.30 = 4.30$$

If 25 mL of water is added to this buffer to increase the volume to 0.125 L, the concentration of the acid and base decreases proportionally.

$$\frac{0.025 \text{ M HA} \times 0.100 \text{ L}}{0.125 \text{ L}} = 0.020 \text{ M HA}$$

$$\frac{0.050 \text{ M A}^- \times 0.100 \text{ L}}{0.125 \text{ L}} = 0.040 \text{ M A}^-$$

The ratio of $[A^-]/HA$ is now 0.040/0.020 which is the same as before dilution. As a general rule, you can assume that the concentration of acid and base present in solution are the same as the concentrations of each originally added to the solution. This general rule does not hold when the buffer is extremely dilute (when the concentrations of the buffer components are in the region of the K_a value). The values that we plug into the Henderson–Hasselbalch equation have not changed. The pH of the buffered solution will continue to be 4.30.

Addition of a Strong Acid

Next, consider what happens when a strong acid such as hydrochloric acid, HCl, is added to the same buffer. In that case, some of the conjugate base is converted to the weak acid:

$$A^- + HCl \longrightarrow Cl^- + HA$$

This means that the value of $[A^-]$ decreases while the value of $[HA]$ increases. For example, if 0.020 L of 0.025 M HCl is added to 0.100 L of buffer solution that contains 0.025 M HA and 0.050 M A⁻ :

1. We add $0.020 \text{ L} \times 0.025 \text{ M} = 5.0 \times 10^{-4}$ mol of HCl. We also increase the volume to 0.120 L.

2. The original buffer had 0.100 L $\times$ 0.050 M = 5.0 $\times$ 10^{-3} mol of A^-. We will lose 5.0 $\times$ 10^{-4} mol of A^- in the reaction with the HCl, so we are left with 4.5 $\times$ 10^{-3} mol of A^-. The concentration of A^- will now be 4.5 $\times$ 10^{-3} mol/0.120 L = 0.038 M.

3. The original buffer had 0.100 L $\times$ 0.025 M = 2.5 $\times$ 10^{-3} mol of HA. We will increase the amount of HA by 5.0 $\times$ 10^{-4} moles, so we now have 3.0 $\times$ 10^{-3} mol of HA. The concentration of HA will now be 3.0 $\times$ 10^{-3} mol/0.120 L = 0.025 M.

4. The ratio $[A^-]/[HA]$ is now 0.038/0.025 = 1.5, so the pH is calculated to be

$$pH = 4.00 + \log(1.5) = 4.00 + 0.18 = 4.18$$

Despite the addition of 20 mL of strong acid, the pH changes very little.

Methods of Buffer Preparation

There are two methods for preparing buffers. One method is to prepare a buffer by first preparing stock solutions of the weak acid and conjugate base separately (or weak base and conjugate acid) then mixing the calculated amount of acid and base together in the desired ratio. The pH of the buffer is adjusted if necessary. The other method is to begin with a weak acid or base in solid form. The solid is dissolved in water, then strong acid or base (such as hydrochloric acid or sodium hydroxide) is added to attain the desired pH. We will use the first method.

Example: Prepare **0.250 L of formic acid/sodium formate buffer at a pH 4 with a total concentration of 0.0400 M**. Formic acid has a **pK_a of 3.74**. Assume **stock solutions with 0.100 M formic acid and 0.100 M sodium formate** (conjugate base) are available.

$$HCOOH(aq) \ + \ H_2O(\ell) \ \rightleftharpoons \ H^+(aq) \ + \ HCOO^-(aq)$$

1. *Determine the formic acid/sodium formate, [HCOO⁻]/[HCOOH], ratio.* To prepare the buffer we must determine how much of each species, $HCOO^-$ and HCOOH, we need. We do this by first finding their ratio at the desired pH. This requires us to rearrange the Henderson–Hasselbalch equation:

$$pH = pK_a + \log\frac{[HCOO^-]}{[HCOOH]}$$

$$pH - pK_a = \log\frac{[HCOO^-]}{[HCOOH]}$$

We take the antilog of each side of the equation, then calculate the ratio using the known values of pH and pK_a.

$$10^{(pH - pK_a)} = \frac{[HCOO^-]}{[HCOOH]}$$

$$10^{(4.00-3.74)} = 10^{(0.26)} = 1.82 = \frac{[HCOO^-]}{[HCOOH]}$$

or $1.82[HCOOH] = [HCOO^-]$

This means that the concentration of sodium formate should be 1.82 times that of the concentration of formic acid.

2. *Determine the actual concentrations of sodium formate and formic acid needed to make the 0.0400 M buffer.* The concentrations of the two species in the buffer when added together must result in a total buffer strength of 0.0400 M. Therefore,

$$[0.0400 \text{ M}] = [HCOOH] + [HCOO^-]$$

Substituting $1.82[HCOOH] = [HCOO^-]$ into the total buffer concentration equation above and solving for [HCOOH]:

$0.0400 \text{ M} = [HCOOH] + 1.82[HCOOH]$

$0.0400 \text{ M} = 2.82[HCOOH]$

$0.0142 \text{ M} = [HCOOH]$

Now that we know [HCOOH], we can solve for [HCOO$^-$] using the ratio derived from the Henderson–Hasselbalch equation:

$[HCOO^-] = 1.82[HCOOH] = 1.82(0.0142 \text{ M}) = 0.0258 \text{ M}$

3. *Mix the correct amounts of formic acid and sodium formate to give the desired concentration and pH.* Above it was determined that if we made 1 L of solution of the described buffer it would take 0.0142 moles of formic acid and 0.0258 moles of sodium formate. Since we are going to make 0.250 L of solution, we will need just ¼ the number of moles or 0.00355 moles of formic acid and 0.00645 moles of sodium formate. We will prepare the buffer from the stock solutions which are 0.100 M solutions:

Volume of formic acid needed: 0.00355 moles HCOOH × (1 L/0.100 mol HCOOH in stock solution) = 0.0355 L formic acid

Volume of sodium formate needed: 0.00645 moles HCOO$^-$ × (1 L/0.100 mol HCOO$^-$ in stock solution) = 0.0645 L formate

Thus you would mix 35.5 mL of 0.100 M formic acid solution and 64.5 mL of 0.100 M sodium formate solution in a 600-mL beaker and add deionized water to bring the solution to approximately 200 mL, stir, and measure the pH. If the pH is not **4**, you would adjust the pH with a strong acid or strong base. When you have adjusted the buffer to a pH of 4, you would transfer the solution to a 250-mL volumetric flask and bring solution to volume with deionized water.

What the Medical Staff Needs to Know to Administer Corrective Measures

There are three important pieces of data that the medical staff must know to administer the necessary amount of "bicarb" to the patient:

1. The pH of the blood

2. The concentration of $[H_2CO_3]$

3. The concentration of $[HCO_3^-]$

In the emergency room, these questions are answered by measuring the arterial blood gases. In our laboratories, we can answer the first question by measuring the pH of our simulated blood buffer solution with a pH electrode. Knowing the pH of the simulated blood allows us to calculate the ratio of weak acid to weak base using the Henderson–Hasselbalch equation. To find the concentration of each species in the disturbed buffer, we use the calculated ratio and the original total concentration of the buffer.

Determining What Has Happened When a Buffer Is Disturbed

This experiment focuses on restoring the buffering capacity of blood after a disturbance has made the blood too acidic. Using information about the undisturbed buffer, it is possible to find out exactly what happened. Counteracting this disturbance is the basis of a plan to save the patient.

As an example, assume you have **100.0 mL of a carbonate buffer** with a total buffer **concentration of 0.075 M**. The **pK$_a$ of carbonic acid is 6.35**. The undisturbed buffer had a pH of **7.40**. The concentration of carbonic acid and hydrogen carbonate is as follows: $[H_2CO_3]$ = 0.0.0061 M and $[HCO_3^-]$ = 0.0689 M. Therefore, the ratio of $[HCO_3^-]/[H_2CO_3]$ = 11.2.

After the buffer is disturbed with strong acid, you find that the pH is **6.90**. When strong acid is added to the buffer, some HCO_3^- will be converted to H_2CO_3. To correct the disturbance, you must determine the new concentrations of H_2CO_3 and HCO_3^- and then restore the ratio to the original value of 11.2. Restoring the ratio to 11.2 will restore the buffer to a pH of 7.40.

One thing has not changed with the addition of acid—the total concentration of the buffer.

$$[H_2CO_3] + [HCO_3^-] = 0.075 \text{ M}$$

We can calculate the new ratio of $[H_2CO_3]/[HCO_3^-]$ by rearranging the Henderson–Hasselbalch equation:

$$pH = pK_a + \log\frac{[HCO_3^-]}{[H_2CO_3]}$$

$$pH - pK_a + \log\frac{[HCO_3^-]}{[H_2CO_3]}$$

$$10^{pH-pK_a} = \frac{[HCO_3^-]}{[H_2CO_3]}$$

$$10^{6.90-6.35} = \frac{[HCO_3^-]}{[H_2CO_3]}$$

$$3.55 = \frac{[HCO_3^-]}{[H_2CO_3]}$$

We now have two equations and two unknowns. Substitution will allow us to calculate the actual concentrations of H_2CO_3 and HCO_3^-.

$$3.55[H_2CO_3] = [HCO_3^-]; \text{ therefore,}$$

$$3.55[H_2CO_3] + [H_2CO_3] = 0.075 \text{ M}$$

$$[H_2CO_3] = 0.016 \text{ M} \quad \text{and} \quad [HCO_3^-] = 0.075 \text{ M} - 0.016 \text{ M} = 0.059 \text{ M}$$

Restoring the Buffer to the Original Ratio of [base]/[acid]

To restore the buffer to the undisturbed pH, we need to add enough HCO_3^- to bring the ratio of $[HCO_3^-]/[H_2CO_3]$ back to the value of 11.2. Let's assume that we have a 0.50 M solution of HCO_3^- at our disposal to restore the buffer. We must set up an expression to find the volume of HCO_3^- needed for restoration.

We substitute the current number of moles of HCO_3^- and H_2CO_3 into the ratio. We also add an expression that represents the amount of 0.50 M HCO_3^- that must be added to achieve the desired ratio, 11.2.

$$\frac{([HCO_3^-]_{\text{(after disturbance)}} \times \text{Vol. of buffer}) + (0.50 \text{ M } HCO_3^- \times \text{Vol. needed to restore buffer})}{([H_2CO_3]_{\text{(after disturbance)}})(\text{Vol. of buffer})} = 11.2$$

$$= \frac{[HCO_3^-]}{[H_2CO_3]}$$

Inserting our values into the equation:

$$\frac{(0.059 \text{ M } HCO_3^- \times 0.100 \text{ L}) + (0.50 \text{ M } HCO_3^- \times X \text{ L})}{(0.016 \text{ M } H_2CO_3 \times (0.100 \text{ L})} = 11.2$$

where X is the liters of 0.50 M HCO_3^- needed. Solving for X, we find that we must add 0.037 L or 37 mL of 0.500 M HCO_3^- to restore the buffer to a pH of 7.40.

Procedure

Data Collection

Lab work is performed in groups of 3 or 4 students. Each person must record a complete set of data in his/her notebook and turn in the duplicate copy on the perforated pages at the end of lab.

You will be measuring pH of buffer solutions with a pH electrode connected to the LabQuest interface.

Part I. Simulating the Blood Buffering System

The carbonic acid–hydrogen carbonate buffer system of the blood is difficult to study in a general chemistry laboratory because the system rapidly loses carbon dioxide (CO_2) to the atmosphere. Therefore, in this lab you will work with a buffer that behaves similarly to the carbonic acid buffer: a phosphate buffer system where the pH is buffered by the equilibrium between the acid, dihydrogen phosphate $H_2PO_4^-$, and its conjugate base, hydrogen phosphate, HPO_4^{2-}. You will eventually be confronted with a solution of this simulated blood buffer that has been disturbed by cardiac arrest. To get ready for the challenge and to increase your understanding of buffers, you will show that you can prepare a phosphate buffer.

Calibrating the pH Electrode

The pH electrode is kept in a tube of storage solution next to the computer; connect the probe to the LabQuest 2 interface via the CH1 port. Connect the LabQuest to a power adapter and plug it in. Turn on the LabQuest by pressing the power button.

You will need jars of pH 4 and 10 buffer for a two-point calibration of the electrode. Use the buffer solutions in the jars provided. Do not transfer the buffer solutions to another container. Do not discard the buffer solutions.

1. At the top of the display, click **Sensors > Calibrate > 1 CH1: pH**. This will open a new window called **Sensor Settings**. Click **Calibrate Now**.

2. Remove the pH electrode from the storage solution. Rinse the electrode with deionized water (use a small beaker to collect the rinses), blot it dry using a Kimwipe and place the electrode in the pH 4 buffer solution. Swirl the jar gently for 15 seconds. In the box for **Value 1:** enter a value of "**4**" and click **Keep** to store the calibration point.

3. Remove the electrode from the pH 4 buffer, rinse it with deionized water and blot dry. Place the tip of the electrode in the pH 10 buffer solution and swirl gently for 15 seconds. Enter "10" as the value for **Known Value 2** and click **Keep** to store the second calibration point. Click **OK**.

4. Remove the electrode from the pH 10 buffer, rinse with deionized water and place the electrode in the tube of storage solution or deionized water. Your pH electrode is now calibrated.

Preparing Simulated Blood Buffer

Your task is to prepare **250 mL of phosphate buffer (simulated blood)**. **The pH must be 7.4** and have a total buffer concentration of **0.100 M**.

You will have available to you:

The acid, **0.25 M potassium dihydrogen phosphate** (KH_2PO_4),

and

The conjugate base, **0.25 M potassium monohydrogen phosphate** (K_2HPO_4).

Phosphoric acid has three acidic hydrogens and thus has three values of pK_a: 2.1, 6.80, and 12.3. You will use the **pK_a value, 6.80**, which is nearest to the pH of the buffer that you will prepare.

1. Calculate the amount of the acid and base needed to prepare **250 mL** of the simulated blood buffer. See **Methods of Buffer Preparation**.

2. Use graduated cylinders to add the calculated amount of acid and base to a clean 600-mL beaker.

3. Add deionized water to the 200 mL mark on the beaker and stir with a magnetic stirrer.

4. Rinse the electrode and place it in the buffer solution. Do not allow the stir bar to hit the electrode. Measure and record the pH of your buffer. If the buffer is not within a pH of **7.30 and 7.50**, add 6 M HCl or 6 M NaOH dropwise to adjust the pH following the steps below. Perform this adjustment carefully:

    a. Keep the electrode in the buffer to continuously monitor the pH. Stir the buffer continuously.

    b. Add one drop of 6 M hydrochloric acid (if the pH is too high) or 6 M sodium hydroxide (if the pH is too low); stir for at least 30 seconds to allow the pH to stabilize.

    c. Continue adding 6 M HCl or NaOH dropwise until the pH of the buffer is between 7.30 and 7.50.

5. Transfer your buffer to a 250-mL volumetric flask. Use a wash bottle to rinse the 600-mL beaker twice with deionized water and transfer the rinses into the volumetric flask. Bring the solution to volume with deionized water. Mix the buffer by covering the top of the flask tightly with Parafilm and invert several times.

6. Pour 20 mL of the buffer into a 100-mL beaker. Stir the solution with a stir bar. Check the pH of the buffer and record your results. If the pH of the buffer is not within a pH of **7.30 and 7.50**, check your calculations and prepare the buffer again. **Save this solution for Effect of Adding Strong Acid.**

Effect of Adding Strong Acid

You will be comparing the pH of deionized water and buffer after adding strong acid. **TIP**: You must measure the pH of deionized water immediately because the water will begin to pick up carbon dioxide from the air. The carbon dioxide will react with water to form carbonic acid.

1. Rinse and blot dry the electrode.

2. Obtain 20 mL of deionized water from the faucet in a 50-mL graduated cylinder. Pour into a clean, dry beaker.

3. Quickly measure and record the pH of the deionized water.

4. Using the micropipet, quickly add 100 µL of 6 M HCl to the deionized water. Stir and allow the solution to come to a stable pH value. Record the pH.

5. Rinse and blot dry the electrode.

6. Place the beaker of buffer saved from the preparation of the buffer on the stir plate and begin stirring the buffer. Do not allow the stir bar to hit the electrode.

7. Measure and record the pH of the simulated blood buffer.

8. Add 100 µL of 6 M HCl. Stir the buffer and allow the solution to come to a stable pH value. Record the pH of the buffer after the addition of acid.

Effect of Dilution

1. Add 20 mL of the simulated blood buffer and a stir bar to a clean, dry 600-mL beaker.

2. Rinse and blot dry the electrode.

3. Measure the pH of the simulated blood buffer; you may have to tip the beaker to immerse the electrode in the solution.

4. Add 25 mL of deionized water and measure the pH again.

5. Repeat this process, successively adding 50 mL, 100 mL, and 200 mL of deionized water. See Table 11.1 below.

Table 11.1. Effect of Dilution.

Volume of Water Added to Buffer (mL)	Total Volume of Solution (mL)	pH
0	20	
+25	45	
+50		
+100		
+200		

Part II. The Treatment Protocol

Consider the following critical care question:

A patient is 6-feet tall and has a body mass between 190 and 225 lb so their blood volume is approximately 5.8 L. The patient's blood pH, due to cardiac arrest, is 7.00. How many mL of 84 mg/mL bicarbonate must be administered intravenously to bring the patient's blood pH to between 7.35 and 7.45?

We will simulate the preceding conditions using your simulated blood buffer solution, but with a much smaller volume of solution at higher concentrations of the acid and conjugate base.

GIVEN:

- Volume of blood buffer = 100 mL

- pK_a = 6.80

- pH of blood after disruption = ??? Your teaching assistant will disturb with 6 M HCl.

- A solution of 0.50 M HPO_4^{2-} to restore the pH of the blood buffer to 7.40.

1. Measure 100 mL of your simulated blood buffer into a clean, dry 250-mL beaker. Add a stir bar and begin stirring the solution. Rinse the electrode and lower into the buffer solution.

2. Your teaching assistant will disturb your simulated blood buffer with drops of 6 M HCl.

3. Stir the buffer and allow the pH value to stabilize. Record the pH of the disturbed buffer.

4. Calculate the amount of **0.50 M HPO_4^{2-}** (disodium hydrogen phosphate) necessary to restore the 100 mL of your patient's blood to a pH of 7.40. You will have 30 minutes to save your patient.

5. When your calculations are complete, obtain the necessary volume of **0.50 M HPO_4^{2-}** in a graduated cylinder. Ask your teaching assistant to observe as you add, all at once, the HPO_4^{2-} calculated. Stir the solution. Allow the pH value to stabilize and measure the pH. If your pH is in the target range, congratulations, you have saved your patient!

Cleanup and Storage of Equipment

Rinse the stir bars, burets, and pipets with deionized water and return them to your TA. Return any volumetric glassware to the cabinets in the back of the room.

Disconnect the electrode and return it to the tube of storage solution. Close Logger *Pro*. Shut down the LabQuest by selecting the Home icon then System > Shut Down > OK. Return the LabQuest and power adapter to the box on your bench.

Keep your safety goggles on until you have finished cleaning and are leaving the lab. Lock your lab drawer before you leave.

Data Analysis and Results

Show ALL calculations for preparing a buffer in Part I, the treatment protocol in Part II, and the pH of your final buffer in Part II.

The Laboratory Report

Your group is to prepare one lab report following the guidelines and outline described on pages x–xii.

Remember, it is your responsibility as a group to ensure that everyone whose name is on the report participated as fully as possible in the project.

The due date and time will be communicated to you by your instructor. Reports will usually be due at the beginning of lab the week after the experiment was completed.

Lab Notebook Pages

Before you leave lab, turn in the duplicate pages from your lab notebook where you recorded data and observations as you completed the lab work.

NOTES